THE OTHER SIDE OF PERFECT

Discovering the Mind-Body Connection to Healing Chronic Illness

Debbie Emick

ISBN:
978-1-7358230-2-7 (Hardcover)
978-1-7358230-1-0 (Paperback)

Library of Congress Control Number: 2020918385

Front cover image and Book Design by Matt Stone.

Printed by Go Bucket Yourself, in the United States of America.

First printing edition 2020.

1000 Hopkins Ave. Rocky Ford, CO 81067

gobucketyourself.com/books

To Claire and Lilah, the loves of my life. May knowing my story help you to write your own.

To Chris, who made it possible and proved that we can grow together and not apart.

"I'll tell you right now, the doors to the world of the wild self are few but precious. If you have a deep scar, that is a door. If you have an old, old story, that is a door. If you love the sky and the water so much you almost cannot bear it, that is a door. If you yearn for a deeper life, a full life, a sane life, that is a door." - Clarissa Pinkol Estés

Table of Contents

Table of Contents (cont.)

THE OTHER SIDE OF PERFECT

Discovering the Mind-Body Connection to Healing Chronic Illness

True Story

She grew up WILD.
dirt road, country lane—wild
ducking under barbed wire fences—wild
jumping out to open the gate—wild
teeth rattling, truck bed riding, bumping through the field—wild
climbing up on the roof with her brother—wild
throwing feed off the tailgate, calling the cows—wild
wide open as far as the eyes could see—wild
until she didn't

She grew up CITY.
key around her neck, home alone after school—city
duplex, townhouse—city
no backyard (or front yard)—city
babysitter named TV—city
where did her brother go—city
asphalt and sidewalks and stop lights—city
never meet your neighbors—city
shopping malls and trendy clothes—city
until she didn’t

She grew up ALONE.
goodbye dad, goodbye mom—alone
case of beer but the money's run out—alone
head in a book to escape—alone
living in a friend's spare bedroom—alone
working 'til close on a school night, no curfew—alone
light a cigarette for the drive home—alone
her brother found another way out—alone
cap and gown, gonna leave town—alone
until she didn't

She grew up AFRAID.
married, white picket fence—afraid
people pleasing, never complain—afraid
no eye contact, always look down—afraid
works so hard to prove her worth—afraid
depends on no one, lets no one near—afraid
hustles 'til her body aches—afraid
never asks herself what she wants—afraid
perfectionism her addiction—afraid
until she wasn't

She grew up.

She grew up REAL.
just stopped hustling—real
worthy as is—real
never perfect anyway—real
makeup's off, no more masks—real
slow down, get quiet, listen for the truth—real
dig it all up and deal with it—real
found love for herself too—real
curiosity her new friend—real
still a work in imperfect progress—real

Prologue: Dear Mom and Dad

"Out beyond ideas of right-doing and wrongdoing, there is a field. I will meet you there. When the soul lies down in that grass, the world is too full to talk about." - *Rumi*

Dear Mom and Dad,

I want you to know that I did my very best to tell only my story. It was not my intention or desire to tell the stories of others. This was difficult, as the deepest truth of my story—the one that fought so hard to break free from deep within me that at moments it spilled out as though there was no other way—that one was very closely entwined with the two of you. Some of my story will always be some of yours.

The telling of my story was done only from the purest of intentions—love. This is my deepest act of love yet—love for myself, for my daughters and the future health of the family that guides them, and love for the both of you, too. It is only out of love that I show you myself, all of me. There's no hiding here, no pretending, just an authentic admission of all that I truly am. This can only be done through love and trust—trust that whatever reaction comes will be to the eventual benefit of all involved. It is my hope that telling my whole story—allowing myself to be seen—will bring us closer, no longer separated by falsehoods we think protect us. I trust that you will do what's best for you in response.

I understand that it's my story. Your story may very well be different. That's okay with me. Your story is not mine to tell, after all. With my story, I release any expectation of or attachment to either of you in any regard. Your choice to read, react, and respond to it is entirely your choice. You must do whatever is best for you.

I'll hide no more. I won't apologize for being open and honest and free with myself and with others. I'll do my best to be authentically me from here on out. When a door to my wild self presents itself, I'll open it. I'm opening it. I'm stepping through.

REALly Yours,
Debbie

Introduction

"Someone I once loved gave me a box full of darkness. It took me years to understand that this too was a gift." - Mary Oliver

I was standing in my kitchen when I got the news. I had just started making dinner, having only arrived home from work minutes before. It was dark outside, and my daughters—ages six and one at the time—were in another room playing together. The caller I.D. on my phone let me know that it was my doctor. The uncommon nature of a doctor's phone call at this time of night meant I answered quickly.

There would not be a lot of small-talk. She got right to the point, wanting to get home to her own dinner, I assumed.

"I'm surprised to tell you that the blood-work you requested was positive," she said.

"What does that mean?" I asked.

"Well, the ANA marker, the one I ordered to check for Lupus, was positive. That means you could have Lupus, or you might not. I'll refer you to the rheumatologist closest to you right away. He'll be able to see you soonest. It will take months to get an appointment with the other specialists in Colorado Springs or Denver. His office will call to schedule the appointment. Then he'll be able to order other tests to find out exactly what's going on."

All I knew to answer was, "Okay."

"You know," she went on, "I have a friend that has Lupus. It's not that bad for her. She just has to wear really warm gloves in the winter and she's fine. She doesn't have any other symptoms. It might not be *that* bad. There's still a chance that the pain in your hip is bursitis like I thought. Anyway, the specialist will be able to tell you."

We politely thanked each other and hung up the phone. I couldn't help feeling much less surprised by a positive result than my nurse practitioner, from whom I had requested the tests just a couple of days before. A lot led up to that visit.

When I went in to see her, I explained the strange blood work that had been mentioned after the birth of both of my daughters. I let her know that I never really questioned it or dug deeper into what had been alluded to because I was busy taking care of newborns and it was never an issue until now. I told her about taking up marathon training with my husband, out of friendly competition, many months before; how I enjoyed it more than expected and had developed a regular practice of long, outdoor runs. I explained that suddenly, I found myself unable to run at all, that even walking down the street near my house was too painful. I told her about a couple of other symptoms—bruising, hair loss, lethargy—but mostly I kept it short and sweet. While she poked around on my sore hip, moving my leg around at the same time, I asked her if she could order any tests for Lupus. She did so, at my insistence, but let me know she was fairly confident I was just experiencing what it's like to be in an aging body. At barely over thirty years old, I had a different idea of aging.

What I didn't tell her in the exam room that day, were all the other symptoms I'd been struggling with that summer before the appointment. I never mentioned how mowing the lawn made my wrists and elbows hurt so badly that I couldn't push a shopping cart at the grocery store for several days after. I didn't want to get into just how miserable I'd been on a recent hike to the top of a Colorado "fourteener" (meaning elevation of at least 14,000 feet). Though I'd done many similar hikes previously, I could barely make it down this mountain. I was the last person in our group, which included my fifty-something aunt-in-law, to the car at the trailhead below. Each step down sent shooting pains up my legs, through my knees, and to my hips. I could only move at a snail's pace. I intentionally didn't tell her about no longer being able to braid my daughter's hair because of the stiffness and pain in my fingers and wrists. There was more. I left a lot out.

Over the next few years, I would learn much more about what was really going on with my body. There would be a fairly consistent stream of diagnoses, misdiagnoses, and prescriptions directed my way. I would go on to learn about another blood marker signaling the presence of multiple autoimmune diseases called RNP, this one more rare than the previously found ANA. That was apparent by the look on the doctors' faces and the sound of their voices when they brought it up. This positive result, correlating to the presence of multiple autoimmune diseases, was just the next of many positives I had not planned on hearing after my name or including in the future I envisioned.

What would become clear over the years following that first, after-hours call from a doctor, was that there was no one prescription or combination of prescriptions that would cure what was ailing me. This was not for lack of trying. My first rheumatologist had me taking seven different prescriptions daily. Though I searched and tried so many quick fixes and magic bullets, there was not a single one that could fix the damage continuing to be done to my body.

It was only after all of the pills and quick fixes and magic bullets failed to take my pain away, to repair the physical damage to my organs, that true healing could even begin. After exhausting every superficial treatment and intervention I could find or was recommended, I found myself at the lowest point of all—rock-bottom, the darkest night of my soul, no purpose or hope for moving forward. Only then, could I even begin to have an honest look at what had gotten me to that point and what might possibly help me out of the depths of that place.

It was the darkness that presented me with my greatest gifts to date. Darkness taught me what healing really means. All of the years of feeling a victim to tests, diagnoses, and symptoms were continually leading me to the box of darkness given to me decades before I learned words like autoimmune or Lupus. My physical health merely pointed to that gift. I had to do the work of uncovering what it meant to heal. Doing so required resurrecting the past, decidedly choosing to play victim no longer, and using the very darkness itself to become the hero of my own story, no longer waiting for *something* or *someone* to save me. It was the past that showed me the light that would lead me out of the darkness. It was the darkness that became my greatest gift.

This is the story of the long and winding road, the road that led me deep into the past, where my wild heart began, and slowly wound its way back to the present—the road that connected the darkness and the light. This is the story of how I ultimately found that light within me.

City

I knew it was over. My life, the one so familiar to me for the past few years, was dying in that little, white two-door car while I sat helplessly in the passenger seat. It was back there, down the two-lane Colorado Highway 50 behind us, fading into the distance—my dad and brother, home, our happily ever after, my comfortable bedroom at the top of the stairs. What exactly happened I didn't know, but I knew that I hated the feel of the cheap, faded blue cloth interior on my summer skin. Where did Mom get this car anyway? Why did she need a new car to run away? I hated the stubbed out butt of the cigarette in the ashtray, the one with the brown paper on the filter. Mom didn't smoke cigarettes with a brown filter, neither did Dad.

Later that day, just a couple of months past my eleventh birthday, my life died another death when we pulled up to the four-plex apartment on the wrong side of town, Pueblo—a two-hour drive. I felt it as I walked to the top of the stairs and through the door on the upper right, seeing the long and dirty shag carpeting that used to be white. Or was it green? I felt it dying, my old life. The comfort and security and any normalcy I enjoyed in the previous years were lost to me now. As I walked around, tears pooling in my eyes, seeing the green, speckled Formica countertops, a layer of grime in any crack, I knew that I would live more lives. I felt that too. That life we left behind though, the one that vanished in the rearview mirror hours before, that one was forever gone.

Almost immediately a dirtiness began to take its place. It wasn't like the layers of dirt in the apartment I now found myself in—years of unexcavated filth of all the people that once called the apartment home. I felt a kind of dirty that couldn't be seen, deep down inside. I would spend the next decades of my life hiding it, ignoring it, picking at it until it scabbed and bled, trying to scrub it away, but I never really learned how to clean up that shameful dirt until I heard those words from a doctor, my doctor, decades later, "*Someday...*" my pulmonologist would say, as he walked out the door, not finishing his sentence because it was easier to let me fill in the pieces and define the word myself.

Someday (def): of or referring to an inexplicit point in the future in which

a) I'll need to be intubated.
b) My lungs will at least require stents.
c) It's doubtful I'll be a candidate for a lung transplant.
d) It's possible I'll just quit breathing altogether.

This may not have been a city by most people's standards, but to this dirt road, wild-born girl, this was as city as I could imagine. I would begin to find a way through here, but I'd never find a way to settle, not in the way I'd found "home" before. Instead, I found a new way here, learning to be friends with those of a different soul, not the wild I'd left behind. These friends taught me about wearing bras and makeup and making my hair just so. I learned that looking a certain way on the outside provided temporary cover for the unclean emptiness I felt deep inside me now.

I learned to hide parts of myself. In this place, smart didn't belong with pretty and cool, so I buried that too. I learned to polish the surface so much, to keep the connection so shallow, that I could fit anywhere with anyone. I mastered the art of averting my gaze, always looking down, to detract attention and connection of others. I began my work of disappearing, fading into the background, never wanting to stand out. This place, this city, was my first teacher in the lessons of detaching, of numbing, and of making myself invisible. This place never became "home," but I carried pieces of it with me for the rest of my life.

Wild

Some people grow up on the wrong side of the tracks, maybe the wrong side of town. Not me. That's not my story. I didn't grow up close enough to town to be on the wrong side of anything at all.

I grew up down a long, dirt road miles from town, in a little, white house—the only house that could be seen for miles in any direction. My bedroom was the small one with the rainbow painted on the blue wall, as though it was plucked right out of the sky itself. At least it seemed that way to a three-year-old, wild girl. I shared it with my brother, who was three years older than me. As I grew older, I'd hear stories of how patient he was with me at this age, the way he'd repeatedly distract or move me away from the meticulously arranged toys and blocks I'd just demolished.

The bathroom at the farmhouse was the one and only place I ever got my mouth washed out with soap, for what I can't quite remember, but it must have been bad.

I stood in the bathroom, shoulders slumped so that my eyes were staring at my feet, covered in white, footie pajamas, my brother at my side. Whatever the reason we were there *must* have been *his* fault. Our mom was at the sink, a white bar of soap in hand. She wet the bar and both toothbrushes under running water, scrubbed the brushes on the damp bar of soap, and handed them to us. My brother knew exactly what to do with it, his skill giving him away. He took the brush and began scrubbing inside his mouth, a sour look on his face. I just held mine. Though I saw what to do, I couldn't quite bring myself to touch that brush to my teeth. My mom had to do that. I knew this was just as punishing for her, too.

After, we would sit on the edge of the bed in the bright room next door to the bathroom, my brother and I. I cried—that breath-catching cry that sounded like I was gasping for air—while my brother comforted me, telling me it wasn't worth crying over at all. "Please stop crying, Debbie," he'd plead.

I always cried. Our mom was probably doing the same in the kitchen, where she now hid. We could only guess. She always cried too. Maybe washing our mouths out with soap was supposed to make us clean again. Maybe it was meant to make us afraid to do dirty things like saying dirty words. Maybe it was supposed to fill us with fear of doing anything dirty at all. Most likely, it was just something our mom thought or heard she was supposed to do when her kids cursed or talked back, being barely twenty-five herself. If clean was anything like the taste of my toothbrush with suds from that bar of soap on it, I didn't mind being dirty at all. I certainly didn't want to be washed clean again.

—

We moved down the road the next year when I was four, leaving those sudsy memories in the past. Two miles south and three miles east on dusty county roads, just about as far south and as far east as you could go and still be in Colorado. We turned into the driveway of the green, metal-sided trailer house recently vacated by my grandparents—the ranch house—a mansion compared to the two-bedroom farmhouse we left behind. It wasn't just a house. It was a house with a barn where cows calved babies and my dad milked our goat and milk cow. Beyond the barn were corrals, where we collected the cattle to brand and doctor them. We called this "working cattle." There were pens that held a fair share of them as well, for feeding in the winter when the fields no longer provided. There was even a big, metal barn that could house tractors and other equipment, and a few bins for storing grain each season until the prices were right to sell. For my brother and me, the chance of getting bored was rare in this new place to call home.

It was here that I heard the words, "Stop running in and out!" more times than I could count. In this kitchen, our mom made strawberry milk and bowls of sliced peaches drizzled with sweet cream—real peaches and cream—just for us. I ate it and thought I might be taking little bites of heaven in every spoonful. I carried the memory of the smell and taste and sight of that bowl with me all the way into adulthood, never quite able to recreate its magic again.

So many memories we took with us from this place, my brother and me, like spending cold mornings standing on the bench pick-up seat beside my dad bumping through fields "checking cattle." We sat on the tailgate throwing large, green cylinder-shaped pellets of food called cake, off the pick-up bed and into the field, as the cows made a slow line behind us to get their winter supplement of food. We giggled and grinned while our mom sped (24 miles) to town over the long, dirt road, going up and down over the hills as the motion made our stomachs feel like it fell to our feet. "Did it tickle your tummy?" Mom always asked. "Yes," we'd laugh back.

We learned and knew well what it was to be a child in this place, eating sugar-laden cereals of the 1980s and making the trip to town dressed up in our homemade Halloween costumes. We spent our days with little care of what it meant to be an adult—not even occurring to us to acknowledge it.

In this wild place, it never occurred to us to think about things like having more money or better clothes or a nicer car. We dreamed of nothing better than spending our days ducking through barbed wire fences or climbing to rooftops, even if the spoils of our adventures were scrapes and bruises and (once) a broken arm. We were too busy, in our boots and jeans, sitting on the top of the metal corral beam and watching our dad, granddad, and uncle work cattle. Then we'd jump to the ground, dirt dusting up like a cloud in the dry soil, as we made our way to the next adventure.

I fell in love with my parents here, in the wild. In this place where I learned some unshakable truths; my parents' love for me was without question, and my life was rooted in this connection to simplicity, hard work, and the quiet solitude of wide-open spaces I carried with me wherever I went. I needed these things through the transitions in my life. I used them to bring me back to what I knew to be true when everything else in my life seemed to be an affront to the truth.

Some places settle deep in the heart and soul—their people, landscapes, and familiar comfort making them more than just a *place.* They make them *home.* Wild would always be home for me. I felt it not only in my heart but deep in my soul when I left and returned again. A piece of me would always be there.

The time came when my parents made their way to something they considered better. My brother and I could think of nothing better than being in wild places, the only type of place we'd known, but our parents disagreed. The years added wants and desires to the hearts of our mom and dad. They wanted more. They wanted different. They wanted things that they had put off after the unexpected surprise of their first child and building the family that followed.

City: More

Just a year or so later, we left the wild, the four of us together, in our parents' search for more. Still, my brother and I brought wild with us, our young hearts full of hope and trust and innocence that would not be snatched away. We moved to a college town, Greeley, five hours north of that little, metal trailer where I drank strawberry milk until my belly was full and bloated, and the dips and crests of the dirt roads tickled my tummy.

I shared a bedroom with my brother again, in a two-bedroom duplex on a city street. I didn't really understand what a duplex was. I was just four-years-old. I did understand that there were neighbors and people near, when before none could be found for miles in any direction. I rode my tricycle up and down the sidewalk in front of our new home, to the stop sign and back. The patterns and people and chain-link fences I saw along the way brought me no surprise after the countless times I made the trip. I went to preschool now—my only school previously being the fields and dirt roads that surrounded the ranch, my desk the bench seat of the pickup. In this place, I had a teacher and classmates while my mom went to work selling light fixtures at a lighting store and my dad went to college to become an accountant. Sometimes, I rode the bus from the preschool to a gymnastics or dance class before going home, something I'd never done in the wild.

We lived in this place for a while, then moved to Canyon, Texas, where my dad finished school. None of this mattered to me, not really. I didn't know any better or any different. I was happy. I was wild. I was free, as long as I had my mom and my brother and my dad. I didn't know that any of that could be taken away. Still so young, so naive, I had no sense that life, years, and people could be thieves, stealing it all away. The temporary quality of these things—the wild, happiness, freedom—that they could simply vanish like the setting sun on the prairie horizon, was a lesson saved for another time yet to come.

Wild: Foundation

"Of all the paths you take in life, make sure a few of them are dirt." - Unknown

The wild was a place that existed in my heart. It was always there, even after I buried it so deep in darkness that I thought I'd forgotten it completely. I would come to learn that it could be resurrected. It also held a space physically, on the dust-blown planes of Southeastern Colorado.

Driving south, out of the sleepy, little prairie settlement we called "town"—Springfield, Colorado—led to a flat world of open fields as far as eyes could see. Which road to take out of town was never a question. Just one paved, two-lane highway could be found leaving in either direction, north or south. About ten miles south, lay a dirt road pointing east. I didn't know the name of the road, because that turn was so deeply etched in my memory there was no need to know what it was called. There wasn't anything in particular that differentiated it from all the other county dirt roads that covered these plains in a one-mile by one-mile grid. I knew it though. This road was where the truck always slowed as it veered to the far right shoulder, making the turn as we got closer to the wild, my wild.

We bumped along, a little slower now on dirt, the dust kicking up in a cloud behind us. We turned two more times, south then east again, before arriving. I anticipated each turn, the memory of the few houses, trees, and water tanks that marked the land were seared into my memory forever. It was always the same. The typical changes that marked a city over time didn't apply here. After our final eastward bend, we came down from one hill and up over another. That up and down marked the transition into the unmistakable soil of the Sand Arroyo, an ancient riverbed long since stripped of its water leaving only a beach-like fine, sandy soil and countless arrowheads behind. This landmark was the inspiration for the name my granddad gave the ranch, the wild place I called home—Sand Arroyo Ranch. When we finally turned into the big driveway, big enough for any farm equipment to pull in and out, I felt it again—that long exhale of home, freedom—regardless of how many moves or years had passed.

When I was younger, it was here that I found giant mounds of seed, called milo, piled up after harvest. I couldn't resist climbing to the top of the red-orange cone that glowed like the color of sunrise. My feet sinking in the quicksand of small, round seeds as I made my way to the top. Then the tiny grains settled into my socks and the pockets of my jeans and through an unguarded waistband and rubbed against my skin. I stayed there anyway, taking in the view while I held handfuls of the feed in front of me and watched them slip through the cracks between my fingers like grains of sand. Too soon the dust from the milo found its way to my eyes and through my nose and against my skin. The immediate itching and sneezing effect of this dust forced me to slide to the bottom of the hill, only adding to its effects. Reaching the bottom and heading off toward the corrals, I knew the discomfort was worth the lingering sensations left on my skin.

The corrals were a well-planned series of pens, made of rough and dark metal pipes and an area leading to the chute fully lined with tall metal panels to move the cattle into a single-file line and block their view, calming them. I made my way to the top rail, the bumpy and gritty texture of the iron grabbed and snagged on my jeans. When I was daring enough, I jumped all the way to the ground on the other side. This trick made me feel quite wild indeed.

Somewhere, within the pens and corridors and chutes of the corrals, I found the others. My dad, mom, brother, uncle, aunt, cousins, grandparents, their friends—all or some were sure to be within, depending on the size of the job for the day. I did my best to stay out of the way of the herd being ushered through the stalls. Sometimes I even found just the right place to help too.

There was not a lot of communication in this work, not verbal anyway. My family knew it so well, it was often done in silence. A simple nod or narrowing of the eyes in one direction or the other said much more than I was able to understand at a young age. Not being as familiar with the routines they all fell into, the muscle memory they developed for this work, I only heard yells when I failed to meet unspoken expectations. Sometimes I stood in the wrong place, scaring one cow in the wrong direction. This undoubtedly caused a chain reaction, like dominoes, that lead to the whole group falling back and forth in confusion. At those times, I knew it was best to go find another place to occupy my time, out of sight of the group.

Other times, I guessed right. I was in the right spot at the right time. Somehow I kept the odd stray steer from escaping through an overlooked hole and inadvertently saved the day. On those days, I stuck around. Maybe I even earned a more advanced job like holding an electric prod or handing an adult a syringe or snips at the chute, jobs I later grew into as I got older and returned for visits. Those were good times too. From that view, I watched as the chute opened and the cow made its way out as quickly as possible, the ranch dog nipping at its heels to spur it along, the distinct smell of burning fur from the glowing branding iron still in the air.

Regardless of my job or location, the same actions repeated themselves over and over again. The cattle were led through the corrals to be pushed and crowded into the pens that narrowed successively until the cows found themselves in a single file line. From there they made their way into a chute that pressed on their sides, firmly holding them in place. Sections of this chute were lowered and raised as my uncle used his pocket knife dipped in Betadine to perform the crude but effective surgery that turned the bulls into steers. Someone else took the branding iron, the end of which had been formed into the brand "R/", from the metal cylinder housing the fire that kept it so hot the end glowed a bright orange. Then the iron was pressed into the fur of the animal's left flank until the hair was singed off and the skin below it burned red. Another hand, worked simultaneously at the head of the animal, where they used long-handled snips to remove the horns and administer any medications or supplements necessary.

These activities never seemed cruel or harsh. I knew my family cared for and respected the lives of the animals that supported us and our family. There was no desire to torture or punish the creatures we depended on for survival. These were just the series of steps required each season when a new set of calves were born or arrived to be raised on the grass that surrounded the ranch. This was a piece of the puzzle that supported life, all of our lives.

It seemed a lot like a party too, from my point of view. Family, friends, and neighbors were all called in to help. They arrived in their work clothes—holey, stained jeans, worn boots, and t-shirts with the sleeves cut off. There were coolers of drinks, one for endless cans of ice-cold beer, another holding cans of sugary sodas. I helped myself as often as I liked. I always hoped to find a green can of Mountain Dew when I reached into the cooler, rarely disappointed.

We all worked in the sun and wind and dirt, sometimes yelling or grumbling, but more often laughing and smiling and hollering. Halfway through the day, someone, usually my grandmother, came with lunch. She pulled up the truck right into the corrals and dropped the tailgate. Then she uncovered whatever dishes had been prepared, casseroles or sandwiches or burgers or hot dogs. Everyone sat on the corrals or tailgates, wherever we could find rest, and ate without worry of the dirty fingers that held the food.

Those were the days. I knew it. I knew by the looks on the faces around me; by their laughter; by the carefree way they carried themselves and went about their work. These were the moments that nourished all those qualities within me, this wild part of me that could never be lost, no matter how hard the world tried to take it from me or I tried to hide it.

City: Separation

"I have my mother's mouth and my father's eyes. On my face they are still together." - Unknown

I rode the bus home from third grade that day with my brother as usual. The bus pulled up to the place we now called home, a rented house far from view of the road behind the expansive front yard that dwarfed it. This is where we moved after the ranch and after the college town—the third stop, a new home in a new state, Canyon, Texas.

White Fence Farms, it was called—the neighborhood we lived in that year. I had my own room, with my own little TV in the corner and a small radio I'd lay on the floor and sing along to my Tears For Fears cassette. I even had my own phone, the kind that plugged into the wall with a really long cord that let me move around the room while I talked. I used it to call my much older, much cooler cousin that lived nearby for a chat.

After completing his accounting degree, dad traded in his multiple shift-work jobs and college classes for one job as one of presumably hundreds of accountants for a very well-known Texas oil tycoon. Mom worked odd hours dispatching for the local police department. Sometimes she was home when my brother and I made the walk down the long, tree-lined driveway into the house. Sometimes she was still at work.

This is why we weren't surprised to find ourselves alone that day after school, coming in, as usual, yelling, 'Mom?' as we entered. I was surprised when I made my way back to the bathroom in my parents' bedroom. I opened the medicine cabinet, in search of something, to find my mother's side empty. Whatever I was looking for wasn't there, my dad's things on the opposite side untouched. I opened drawers and closets, looked around on nightstands and dressers, finding the same over and over again. All of my mom's things were gone.

Rushing out to find my brother who already found an after-school snack and something on the TV, I tried to explain.

"Someone robbed us!"

"What? No one robbed us." A pretty typical reply from my older brother, his response dripping with the annoyance at another ridiculous thing his silly, little sister said.

"Really!" I said louder now, trying to convince him. "All of mom's things are gone. I can't find anything. Someone stole all of mom's stuff."

"Why would someone come in and only take mom's things? That doesn't make sense." A new hint of concern in his changed tone betraying his cool response. "Just wait for mom to get home," his final statement, ending the discussion.

I couldn't help but worry. If someone came in and took all of our mother's possessions, they may have taken our mom, too. That was not much of a stretch from my typical line of thought. Anytime my brother and I were left home alone, I made frequent trips to the large living room window overlooking the front yard and drive. I stared out the window in worry that our mom or dad may never return. My brother was used to my worried anxiety. I could be quite annoying to a brother three years older than me. He was used to gruffly telling me they'd come home, nothing bad would happen, and to quit worrying. That didn't stop me from repeating the exchange until exasperated yelling ended the argument.

This time, like all the others, my mom came home. She acted just as annoyed by the questions streaming from my mouth about things stolen or gone and why. She told me we'd talk about it later after my dad got home. That was enough for me. I made my way out back, across the equally proportioned back yard, to the animal stalls and sheds behind it. I liked to climb on top of the tin roof of the stall near the empty corrals to pass the time, singing or talking to myself or just quietly thinking.

When I saw my dad's car pull up, the orange two-door Mustang with white, vinyl seats, I climbed down and ran for home. I was excited to hear what was going on. It must be something good. My brother knew otherwise. He sensed something I wasn't old enough to understand yet. I saw it in the way he reluctantly came out of his room when we were all called together in the living room.

That's where they told us, my brother and me. They said they were going to separate, as though I should know what that meant, as though I could. I knew it must not be good though. The way my mom insisted on holding me tightly on her lap as she and my dad broke the news was a clue. My mom's tears as she rubbed my hand and we talked made me cry too. I was still good at crying.

My brother was good at anger. His anger spread all over his red face, his tightly crossed arms, and slumped chest and shoulders. He had only one question when they asked. "Can I go to my room?" He didn't want to talk. Of course, I knew my brother well. I knew his anger turned to tears only in his room, where no one else could see his perceived weakness. I did have questions. I still needed to know what happened to all of mom's things. Where had they gone?

The answer came soon after when just my mom and I moved all of our things to Columbia, Missouri—hours and hours away from White Fence Farms in Canyon, Texas. We left my dad, my brother. We lived in another duplex, this time by ourselves in a new city and a new state I never even knew existed.

This time I rode the bus to and from school alone. I waited at the end of my new driveway for it to pick me up, made my way to an open seat, and rode the bus full of strangers to school alone, singing Cyndi Lauper's *True Colors* to myself silently. Then I rode the bus home, in the same way, usually unlocking the front door with my key and making my way inside, alone again. I ate Dorito's and drank Dr. Pepper while I did my homework and watched TV until my mom got home.

The fire of my mom's bitterness for supporting my dad while he finished college was dampened by her own choice to attend college in this new place, something she wanted but put off while dad got his degree first. She went to occupational therapy classes during the day and dispatched for the police department at night. For the first time in my life, as an eight-year-old third grader, I often found myself alone—no brother or father there to watch over me or keep me company when my mom was out. Now there was no one to quiet my fears while I looked out the large front window and wondered if my mom would ever return. I often found myself in this place just like that, alone.

Wild: Back Home

"Every soul innately yearns for stillness, for a space, a garden where we can till, sow, reap, and rest, and by doing so come to a deeper sense of self and our place in the Universe." - Anne LeClaire, Listening Below the Noise

I was in the back of the pick-up, in the bed. I was sitting on the bump of the metal wheel-well from the truck's tire. It was a nice bench for my girl-sized behind. Still in third grade, I was back home on the ranch for a visit with my brother and dad. The wind was blowing my hair back out of my face forcefully, tiny bits of sand and gravel it carried with it working their way into my hair and ears and eyes and teeth. I didn't care. My young heart and soul cared not of things like tangles and dirt and discomfort. I just knew I liked the feeling that rose up from within me when I sat back there, while the truck raced along, the way it made me feel connected to the wild that was around me and within me too.

I felt it again when we turned off the road and neared the gate of the barbed wire fence. I was still too young and not quite strong enough to unlatch this gate. It required shoving the old post attached to the gate toward the post that anchored the fence hard enough to take out all of the slack and simultaneously slide the wire loop that secured them together over the top. My dad did that. He was riding shotgun up front in the cab, my uncle at the wheel. Dad threw the gate to the side on the ground, out of the way of the tires, and waited for my uncle to drive through before he secured it once again and jumped back in.

The pickup carried on through the field at a slower pace now. Its four wheels easily found the two, light-colored ruts languidly etched through its center, where the prairie grass no longer spread to cover the dirt below. The grass all around was not such a stark contrast from the dirt in those ruts this time of year. Its yellowish-brown earthy color camouflaged it well with the sandy soil below. We drove along through this field, an even rougher ride than the dirt road we turned from, until we found the group of cows we were there to feed. This wasn't a difficult game of hide and seek, as the two explorers in the cab up front had spent a lifetime at this very chore. They knew all the cows' preferred hiding places.

The cattle, knowing the proximity of their next meal didn't make it hard on us either. As soon as their dramatically contrasting black figures were noticeable, my uncle began honking the horn of the truck in short intervals. The cows, being well-conditioned to this routine, and big fans of the food that followed the honks, answered back in their own long, low call from afar. "Muooaaaa, muooaaaaa." we heard as the cows and their babies discovered their breakfast was coming. Using their inherent manners and forming a line, the cows began to move, following one behind the other, toward the sound of winter's nourishment.

When the pickup got so near the cow in the lead that we could almost reach out and touch her, my dad jumped out of the passenger seat. He walked alongside the lowered tailgate, grabbing bags of feed from the bed. I tried to hand them to him, but we both knew I was no match for their weight. He dumped the cake—green, compressed cylinders of feed I could barely fit in the palm of my hand—out onto the ground in front of the line already formed by the cattle beside the truck. I wasn't sure why they called it cake. I tried it once. It tasted nothing like what its name suggested.

"Eww! Why'd you do that, Debbie?" my brother asked as I spit the green remnants from my mouth. "Gross!"

"It is gross! It doesn't taste like cake at all," I choked back.

He just stared at me with the exasperation of an older brother, constantly surprised by a ridiculous younger sister.

When all the bags were emptied, it was time to make our way back through the pasture road and the gate again. My brother and I did our job of making sure all the empty, brown bags, that were almost as tall as me, were stacked or crumpled and securely weighted with something we found in the rusty truck bed. This ensured they wouldn't be carried away with the wind before reaching the ranch house.

Off we went again. This time our hands sought the warm spaces of our coat pockets, while our hoods offered a bit of protection from the cool air of very early winter. We smiled and laughed at each other as we caught the air in our mouths in big gulps, tongues hanging out like dogs. We were happy to be together again, even if just for a visit.

The pick-up slowed and turned left into the big drive that went around the ranch house in a half-circle, where our uncle now lived with his family. The truck went past the corrals to the east and all the way around the big shop to the south. We sat patiently, while the pick-up pulled up right in front of the house, just outside the yard, where rattlesnakes were found coiled up in the fence corners every summer. My brother and I didn't need any help getting out. We didn't wait for anyone to give us a hand or drop the tailgate again. We just climbed right up on the side of the truck bed from the wheel well that acted as a step, one leg at a time, and jumped off into the dirt below. This was an old habit to us, as familiar an occurrence as putting our boots on when we left the house. Our dad and uncle made their way inside on the cool, early morning to refill their Thermoses of hot coffee. My brother and I ran off to find our own fun, always keeping a close ear and eye on the truck just in case there was more work to be done, never wanting to be left out.

We were home then, in that place—wild and open and free and together again. We had only just begun to know the things that would cut and bruise us deeply, just barely began to close and protect ourselves.

City: Reconciliation

"But over time people break apart, no matter how enormous the love they feel for one another is, and it is through the breaking and the reconciliation, the love and the doubting of love, the judgment and the coming together again, that we find our own identity and define our own relationships." - Ann Patchett, This is the Story of a Happy Marriage

That morning, when I walked into the kitchen of our duplex in Columbia, Missouri, I found my mom with tears streaming down her face. She was holding a letter in one hand and a torn envelope in the other. On the table beside her, lay a long, skinny black velvet box with a gold bracelet inside. From my eight-year-old point of view, it shone as bright as the sun. Fancy, gold bracelets weren't common in our house.

"What's wrong?" I asked, alarm in my voice.

"Nothing, Debbie," she answered back. I heard this phrase often. I asked a lot of questions. I always wanted to know what was wrong.

"Well, why are you crying? Is it bad? And where did you get that bracelet?" A lot of questions.

"No, it's not bad," she answered calmly. She didn't mirror the alarm in my voice. She sounded tired but not sad. I believed her. "I can't explain it all to you now, but I will soon after I talk to your dad," she went on. "He sent me the bracelet."

Not long after I caught my mom crying in the kitchen, my dad would come to move me back to Texas.

My mom and I moved to Missouri after I had already started my third-grade school year in Texas. She started classes right away, at the University. I got to know a new teacher and a classroom full of kids. We had two Christmases that year—one with Mom, one with Dad. Our parents apologized and bought the affections of my brother and me with lots of gifts. They didn't need to. We each got bikes (a first "ten-speed" for me) and Nintendos, among other gifts. Less than a year later, my dad was there, with a horse trailer, loading up all of our things and buckling me in the passenger seat. I finished the school year back in Texas, while Mom finished her semester in Missouri and stayed with a friend. She would join us as soon as she was done.

For a short time, my dad, my brother, and I shared a house while we waited for my mom—a wild and free time. My brother was my frequent babysitter while our dad was at work. During those weeks, my brother secretly adopted a kitten until it was discovered in his dresser drawer. I kept a cup full of powdered sugar in my closet as a nearby snack anytime I needed one. We toasted Pop-Tarts for breakfast and rode his bike home across town after school. I stood on the pegs on his back tire and held tight to the back of his shirt the whole way. We snacked on Pixie Sticks and burned bugs with a magnifying glass. I even learned how flammable aerosol cans are from my eleven-year-old babysitter.

Then Mom came home. She stayed home with me when I was sick, made food that wasn't prepackaged, and packed up all of our things again. That summer, after my dad got a new accounting job at a local feedlot, we moved back to Southeastern Colorado. We were just an hour away from the ranch and the rest of our family now, living in a tiny town called Wiley.

This time, my parents *bought* a house, a real house—two stories, at the end of a cul-de-sac. We had our own yard, a trampoline in the back, and behind that, across the alley, was a little pond and an alfalfa field that stretched on for miles, through my childhood eyes. I loved walking through it in the summer when the hay was full of purple-blue blossoms. My mom didn't have to work now. She cooked dinner that we ate together around the table every night. She had snacks waiting at home for us after school, insisting that we finish our homework before heading out to play. We were a *real* family, again.

As long as the sun was up (but sometimes after sunset) and my homework was finished, waking hours were spent playing and riding bikes with my new friends, Kate and Lillie. On weekends, we packed lunches and set off on adventures along the irrigation ditch by our house to a trestle we called, "Terabithia." Then we spent any night we were able at each other's houses, taking turns having sleep-overs.

Things were good again, as perfect as I could imagine, and everyone was happy. This time seemed like it would never end. I couldn't think of any reason it should.

City: Split Second

"Hurt travels through time. From one person to another this unwanted heaviness moves from the past, into the present, and then into the future." - Yung Pueblo

The next time our family broke apart, there was no conversation, no sit-down in the living room. My brother and I began to piece together clues that it was coming. Maybe that was the intention of our parents, for us to predict the outcome for ourselves, or maybe they were just too tired, too afraid, to explain it all again.

My mother moved upstairs to my little room in our two-story house in Wiley, sleeping on the trundle below my daybed on the nights she slept at home. The summer between my fifth and sixth-grade school year, our parents began fighting openly, something previously saved for behind a closed, bedroom door. For the first time I could remember, those arguments were punctuated with curse words and phrases like, "Shut up!" And once, "Shut the *fuck* up!" I subconsciously learned that loud fighting inevitably led to splitting.

I didn't know for sure, but I thought I could feel it. The time back in the wild, the careless days of childhood in a small town full of friends, that was coming to an end. The time was nearing when we would split again—my brother, my mom, my dad, me. I didn't know why, but I knew the leaving was upon us.

One night, when my mom was out, my dad came up to my room. With tears in his eyes, he apologized. It was years before I understood fully what that apology and the many other apologies to follow were for. I didn't know why at the time, but I felt his pain. I felt it sink deep into my bones. This was a burden I carried my whole life—a deep empathy that caused me to hold onto and identify with the pain, burdens, and afflictions of others—being sensitive. This, too, took decades to understand, and to eventually use as a gift.

I cried then, consumed by his pain, his fear, his regret, and shame. I felt it all, without being able to name it. I wanted to take it all away. Not knowing how, I absorbed it all, carrying the burden of the shame with me now.

We sat there, in the darkness illuminated only by the small lamp in the corner of my room, crying together. I told him that it was okay, that it would all be okay. I didn't know if it was okay or even what okay was. I just knew that's what you say to someone suffering, and I was still full of so much hope that it might be—okay. Hope—that wasn't stripped from me, yet.

City: On The Edge

"Parentified children learn to take responsibility for themselves and others early on. They tend to fade into the woodwork and let others take center stage. This extends into adulthood—adult children may put others' needs before their own. They may have difficulty accepting care and attention." - Kimberlee Roth, Surviving a Borderline Parent

We were standing in the kitchen, covered in the pitch black of night, no light on. It wasn't the first time this had happened, but it was the first time I started to notice the pattern.

I was somewhere on the edge of twelve and thirteen. I'd begun attending Sunday school and church regularly after my mom took a job as the secretary of the First Southern Baptist church on the other side of town. It was her second or third job since moving us to Pueblo, Colorado, just the two of us again. The jobs came after she ran out of money and was forced quit occupational therapy school, for the second time.

I wanted her to go church with me, something in my soul crying out for something to save us both, a place to feel safe and at home. Maybe the church could save us. Maybe the church could give us a place to belong again. I wanted my mom to walk up the stairs and through the doors with me, to shield me from all the long glances that told me I didn't belong. Instead, my mom drove twenty minutes to the church every Sunday morning, dropped me off, and came back to pick me up after it was all over.

I did my best to hide the courage it took to enter the building alone each week and walk up the stairs to that Sunday-school room, the weight of all my parents' shame carried on my shoulders. I went in anyway, my need for revival so strong. The looks of the others seared into me as I sat down. I was good at looking down by then, avoiding eye contact, hiding. They noticed anyway. I pretended I didn't.

"Hello!" the teacher said, her voice lifting in surprise at the end, giving away the judgment she was trying to hide.

They asked more questions. They wanted to know more about this stranger that was so different from them, the one that didn't belong, as though not belonging was like a bad odor I carried with me that they so easily sniffed out. Some scents were fresh and clean, I imagined, not like mine.

I was fully settled in withdrawing at this point. I spent my Sundays in this place and the rest of my free-time holed up in my room highlighting bible passages and writing depressing poems. I spent the year before learning to fit in, trying to change myself to fit this place and pretend that nothing was wrong.

That year broke me, so much so that by my seventh-grade year, my friends at school noticed the drastic change in my behavior and staged an intervention with a "peer" counselor in the office. They surprised me between classes, asking me to follow them to a meeting. We went into a little, windowless room, with a round table in the center. The room was all white, the painted walls and vinyl tiled floors were starkly cold and clean like a hospital. My friends told me about the changes they noticed—too quiet and a general unhappiness. They told me how worried they were. Astute at shutting down, I said nothing, the tears in my eyes were the only clue that I heard their words at all. I stared ahead, feeling betrayed and embarrassed and ashamed all at once. Still silent, I simply got up and left the room, the door open behind me. My friend followed dramatically, apologizing as she walked behind. I never said a word. This became another secret I carried, telling no one, especially my mom.

My mom was standing opposite me now, our backs leaned against the counter in the dark galley kitchen of the two-story townhouse on the busy street where we now lived—just blocks from that first, upper-level apartment in the four-plex with dingy shag carpeting and questionable neighbors that took us away from my dad and my brother—still on the wrong side of town. The friends I had at school lived elsewhere, in communities with names and gates around them. My mom was crying again. There was so much to cry about now. She had been out drinking with Dan—my step-dad—again. It was their every-weekend habit these days.

Mom and Dan met at a party hosted by the parents of my first friend in this city, my best friend, Ruth. Dan was Ruth's alcoholic uncle that came to the party. My mom must have been drawn to him by some invisible magnetic force of codependency. He recently lost his family to divorce and his driver's license to alcohol. Being impossible to live on his own with garnished wages for unpaid child support, court fees from DUI proceedings, and no car or license to take himself to and from work, he moved in with his parents, who chauffeured him around. That is until my mom came along.

He moved in with us just weeks after that party, immediately taking up far more than his fair share of space in the little, dirty four-plex we had moved into just months before. He had few possessions and even less money to contribute, yet he carried with him much more metaphorical baggage than that tiny space would allow. The shag carpeting and old Formica counters felt even dirtier now with him there. My mom and I would learn quickly how to hide and contract to accommodate him.

The following school year, the three of us moved to a townhouse, the one my mom and I stood in now. A short time after, my Great-Grandma passed away, leaving my mom with some inheritance. I never learned how much of an inheritance it was. It wasn't enough to go school shopping before my seventh-grade year, but it was enough to cover a trip to Las Vegas and a set of rings for mom and Dan. They returned married and I withdrew further, disappearing inside my room and inside myself. The wedding added to my search for a savior for us both, my mom and me.

It was in this townhouse that my mom cried to me after a night of drinking. She came home without her drunk, newlywed husband and found the depressive effects of alcohol sinking in. I was her only confidante, her twelve-year-old daughter. She confided her deepest secrets and fears in me, her child, again and again.

Tears were shed and words said that could never be taken back—tales of abortions and Dan and arguments and alcohol and drugs and walking home through the mud by herself, her dirty sneakers on the rug by the door giving that last little bit away.

"God will never forgive me, Debbie!" She wept that night.

"He will, Mom." I pleaded. "He forgives anything. You just have to ask." I was a good student of the church and the Bible. I too had tried washing away the dirt I felt deep inside with God's forgiveness, as though I'd actually done something at such an age to contribute to the hopelessness we found ourselves in.

"Oh, Debbie. You're so strong," my mom answered. "How can you be so strong? What would I do without you?"

These last questions unknowingly and most unintentionally cemented my fate for the years to come. I was strong. I would prove that. I was strong for both of us now. I would require little, and complain even less. Without realizing it at all, I became a parent to myself then. Right then, in that dark, depressing moment in the tiny kitchen, on the edge of twelve and thirteen, I learned how to mother my own mom, without ever learning how to take care of myself first. Who I was, what I wanted or needed, those things were swept away.

—

The wild felt like freedom and truth and sincerity. It was real. It was like the insides matched the outsides in the most honest of ways. I knew the pure joy found in the freedom and truth of the wild—the realness so difficult to find anywhere else. I knew it in my heart. I carried it deep within.

That's why the pain cut so deep when the realities of the city sank in, little-by-little—each compromise, each back-step, each denial of the truth and freedom I'd known before, made the wild harder and harder to find. The pain felt in the many betrayals the city held for me caused me to question if the wild ever existed in the first place.

But it was there, deep within. It called to me from farther and farther away as I quieted it, smothered it, with more and more heartbreaks. It was always there, waiting to be set free.

Maybe this is what made this part of the story so difficult. I had been gifted the treasure of experiencing first-hand what truth was. That knowing made the pain of stripping the truth and freedom that I had away, bit-by-bit, much more painful. This way was an affront to my very nature. All I knew to be true of the world was killed off by lies and denial and alcohol and neglect and abandonment, while I watched.

But there it remained, the wild deep within me, the truth covered by fear. Like a small butterfly silently struggling to find enough space to stretch its wings and move about, it was waiting to be unearthed from the coals and ashes of the past I tried so hard to burn.

City: Cries

"Somewhere along the line, you learned that to express your gut feelings—as in to trust them—would put you into conflict with your attachment environment...[Y]ou adapted by suppressing your gut feelings or by ignoring them." - Gabor Mate, When the Body Says No

There's a stage between living life and the decision to cope by withdrawing from life. This is the cry-for-help stage. I didn't skip that stage. I gave it a solid try with my classmates and teachers at school, my seventh and eighth grade years. I spared my mom from the direct torment—her fragility immediately palpable and my role to protect her now clearly defined.

I cried for help at school, unconsciously or not, perhaps hoping news of these cries might trickle into my mom's awareness. My cries for help took the shape of wearing headphones during pre-algebra lecture, then interrupting with bursts of singing aloud. The cries looked like half-hearted participation in the barrage of spitballs launched at my science teacher daily to open class.

"I'll wait," the science teacher would say in a calm, measured tone, discomfort rumbling below the surface, her red cheeks giving her away.

"I'll wait," she said again.

It was an uncomfortable time. I was either mean and out of control or completely withdrawn. This newfound lack of sound judgment led me to huffing marker fumes one afternoon between classes. Standing in the long hallway lined with lockers, a friend suggested holding a group of uncapped markers closely to our noses, inhaling deeply, and holding a long breath before exhaling. This friend and I took turns passing the markers back and forth several times. It only took that long to feel the effects.

I can't say what I thought as I did so, most likely because I wasn't thinking at all, possibly because the fumes erased any memory I had just before I inhaled. That was the idea I suppose, erase my unpleasant reality, numb it away. What happened after was unforgettable.

I sat in the back of the classroom of my next class with my friend—two pretty, young girls drunk and light-headed on marker fumes. Giggling and goofing off through the entire period, I felt a wave of relief when the bell rang and I had somehow survived the previous hour. Though as I left, the substitute teacher pulled me aside. I wrongly assumed the temporary nature of her role made her clueless. The fuzzy effects of the substance beginning to fade and headache beginning to set in, I realized this to be a ridiculous oversight.

The blond, middle-aged woman shocked me as she described exactly what she knew we'd done. My jaw gaped open as she explained that her other job was teaching prisoners at the facility about thirty minutes down the road. She went on to describe what someone who destroys their brain over and over again, in the way I had just chosen to do, looks and acts like years later. The way they seal their fate in a way she knew I didn't want or intend. She looked at me, holding eye contact. I averted my eyes, choosing to stare at the seam in the shiny, waxed square tiles below our feet.

"You're better than that. Your brain is meant for more than that," she said. "That's what so many of the men I work with, in the prison, have done to themselves over the years, and I could tell you more than you want to know about their lives."

I still couldn't meet her stare in the empty, junior-high classroom, but I felt the truth of her words in my heart. Their impact shone in the tears settling in the corners of my eyes. She didn't send me to the office. She didn't call my mom. She just spoke directly to me, in that classroom lined with empty desks. My cries for help were finally heard, by a substitute teacher. She spoke right to those cries for help in a way no one else in my life had done.

Not like my mom, who laughed when she heard how I was treating my math teacher or that I got a D in Home-Economics.

"I got a D in Home-Ec, too," my mom commiserated.

This substitute teacher didn't act confused or out of touch the way my mom had when she found out that my report card was missing because I threw it away instead of handing it over as instructed, ashamed of the grades I earned. Had the teacher reacted in those familiar ways, my future may have been far different, but she didn't. She spoke to me in a way that said,

I know exactly what you're doing. I see your cries for help, and they're not going to give you what you want or need.

It worked.

I walked out of that classroom, ignoring the laughs from my friend about what had just happened, and the cries for help ceased. I found new friends. I quit picking on teachers, and I started doing my school work again. I quit crying out at all. Where I had been teetering on the edge of experimenting with ways I could control my life, becoming completely out of control in the process, I just stopped. Instead, understanding my cries did not incite the aid I sought, I drew further and further into myself in opposition, until I almost didn't need to exist in the world at all.

Alone: Homeless

"Life had broken much of her but she was there still persisting in the shards of her pieces." - Atticus

Shortly after my mom and I left Wiley and moved to Pueblo, my dad met someone too. By the end of my sixth-grade year, he and his girlfriend planned a wedding and moved in together. Her two daughters, several years younger than me, shared the spare room in the two-story house that no longer felt like it was mine.

Dad's girlfriend, Lynn, was easy to like. She attended my basketball tournaments, bearing gifts. She had a great sense of humor and knew how to have fun. She took my friends and me to the lake along with her daughters on hot summer days. She felt like a big sister or grown-up friend. When Lynn became my step-mom, after their wedding at the Christian church and subsequent honeymoon in Jamaica, things changed quickly. Her easy-going attitude more often turned into irritation or impatience over whatever burden I brought with me when I came for visits. The complaints were directed at my dad, who passed them along to me.

A year later, when my dad got a new job at a Bank in Springfield, they sold that house and moved back to the first town of my childhood—the one near the ranch. My visits became less and less frequent, after the move an additional hour away from where I lived, until visits rarely happened at all.

I was there on Christmas break, in their new home. On this holiday, during my eighth-grade year, I found myself in my brother's bedroom, in a dark corner of the house, a perfect place for a teen-aged boy. I spoke excitedly to my friend Kate, from Wiley, on the phone. We were making plans to get together sometime over the school break.

It wasn't noon yet, the time my dad normally came through the door on his lunch break, but I saw him pull up in his little, white pick-up truck. I kept talking to Kate. I wasn't afraid or weighed down here, not like I was in the city. There were fewer surprises, less alcohol, more money, and less sacrifice at my dad's house. I didn't have to hide as much here, I thought. I didn't belong here fully. It wasn't mine, really, but there was no fear here either.

Something pulled me away from my phone conversation. I said goodbye and hung up as I heard yelling coming from the driveway where dad parked. He stepped out, in his suit and tie. He looked through a furrowed brow at Lynn. She yelled with her hands in the air. I couldn't really hear or understand, but the sinking feeling in my stomach—that heavyweight that I thought I didn't have to carry here—gave away that the fight had something to do with me.

I steered clear and stayed out of the way, something I had a lot of practice doing. Peering through the curtains of the sunken room with stone floors, I did just that. No one knew I was watching while *I'm All Out of Love* by Air Supply played from the cassette player in the background. It was a new favorite song, though it had been released just one year after I was born. My mind quickly went through a list of my actions that morning, after my dad left for work. Everything seemed fine then. Could I have done something wrong in the last two hours? I was used to this mental exercise of searching for what I'd done wrong any time loud voices or tension unexpectedly arose. In these moments when fight-or-flight was naturally triggered, I always chose flight. I got quiet, retracted, and hid, even if my hiding place was only somewhere deep inside myself. I couldn't think of anything I'd done to upset my step-mom.

They were walking now, my dad and Lynn, coming inside. I rushed to busy myself with some pretend thing on the bed, my back to the window now, lest I be caught eavesdropping on their fight. My dad came in the room then, quietly, barely meeting my gaze. That was fine with me. I wasn't much for conversation or eye contact anymore either. Looking down and shutting up were two of my most practiced skills. He told me that we were leaving, just the two of us. I should gather up my things, he explained—put everything I'd brought in the purple, over-sized duffel bag he gave me that year for my birthday.

I did as I was told that morning. I didn't ask why. I put the few things I scattered back into my bag and gave it to my dad to load in the pick-up. I didn't ask him where his bag was. I didn't ask him where we were going either, as we drove down a dirt road outside of town. He finally told me after the silence went on so long it became uncomfortable. He told me we were going to my aunt's house. He was going to take me there to stay for a while. He wasn't sure how long it would be.

"Are you staying too?" I asked as I looked out the window, watching the fields pass by. He didn't need to answer. I already knew.

The rest of that Christmas break, that's how long I would stay with my aunt. That was the answer. It didn't come from my dad. He never called to tell me or came back to get me or explain why I was there. I never asked anything of anyone. I saw my dad again that break, at my Grandmother and Granddad's house, where we all gathered on New Year's Day to celebrate our big, yearly family Christmas—my dad, my brother, cousins, aunts, and uncles. My step-mom and step sisters didn't come. I had a feeling that it was my fault somehow.

It didn't really matter. I loved my family, my grandparents, aunts and uncles, and cousins. They felt like home. They always did. There were never any surprises with them. We always played games and laughed and ate and helped each other clean up. We always had so much to talk about. The conversation was always light and easy, full of air and smiles and jokes. We never talked about dark things there, like why I was staying at my aunt's house or if anyone knew I was staying with her. We didn't talk about why Lynn was absent or if anyone even noticed that she wasn't there. We never spoke about why my mom wasn't there either, why my dad and mom weren't there together anymore. We didn't talk about how my mom married a mean man who drank too much. We didn't mention that my dad married a wolf in sheep's clothing who lost her smile but found a way to yell loud enough to get rid of a thirteen-year-old girl. We never talked about those things there.

Sometimes, privately, my granddad and grandmother would say, "How's your mother doing?" Maybe they really wanted to know, maybe they wanted to hear the truth, but I thought I knew better.

"Good!" I answered quickly. That's what they wanted to hear, I thought, that everything is fine and everyone is good. That's what I did for them, for everyone, for myself as well. I made it all look good, all of it seem fine. That was my gift.

But that year, as the celebration ended, everyone gathered to take a picture together in the living room of my grandparents' house. We rushed to capture the moment before my dad and I loaded in the truck. The camera clicked and tears filled my eyes. I knew. I *knew* even if we didn't talk about it, even if I didn't say it out loud or share it with anyone. I knew exactly what my dad was taking me back to, exactly what I was leaving behind. I looked down and turned away, hiding my tears before anyone noticed. I needed everyone to think everything was fine. That was my job. But my grandparents noticed. They saw otherwise—my granddad and grandmother. I didn't say anything, but I couldn't stop the emotion either, as they tried to comfort me. They assured me that they'd miss me too and I could always come back. They told me that there would always be other visits and more Christmases, that there was always a place for me there.

I never put into words where all the tears came from that night. I just got back in the pick-up and cried silent tears while my dad drove in the dark, through the snow, to meet my mom and make the exchange of goods that was me. We both said *nothing*—that was easier—as the dread of all that I was returning to and all that I was leaving flooded out in tears.

As years went on, there were whispers of what might have been "wrong" with Lynn. I once found prescription pills stating "take for PMS". I never knew women took prescriptions for PMS. I grew to fear becoming an adult and getting PMS. There were other whispers, too. My ears eavesdropped intently, to conversations between my aunts in my grandmother's kitchen, clinging to any explanation. They talked in hushed voices of being sick (people didn't refer to it as mental illness or give it specific names then) or "crazy", and about her family history. In high school, my hunches, based on things I pieced together through small-town gossip, were confirmed. My science teacher made jokes about what he knew about Lynn and her family, after growing up in the same small town that she did. Then, I heard what "ran" in her family—depression, suicide, a "crazy" mother, a "crazy" grandfather. In retrospect, I can see it and name it differently. I can identify her severe mood-swings, her depression, her paranoid behavior. Though at the time, I mistook it all as another confirmation of not being wanted, another reason to feel alone.

Decades passed before I understood that holiday—that it was the final realization that I could never come back, not really. My body, my soul could feel it, even when my mind couldn't make sense of it. I knew without being told, that I had no place, nowhere I could call home, not anymore. The wild was lost to me. The city never was mine. I was alone now—the only place I belonged.

Alone: Loner

"What is your story? It's all in the telling. Stories are compasses and architecture; we navigate by them, we build our sanctuaries and our prisons out of them." - Rebecca Solnit, The Faraway Nearby

I learned to be alone.

I had some experience with this, at the age of eight and nine, during my parents' first separation, when my mother and I so abruptly moved hundreds of miles away. I learned then how to ride the bus to school alone, my big brother no longer with me, then ride that same bus home. Alone. Opening a bag of chips, I sat in front of the thirteen-inch television on a wheeled cart my mom and I could move from the bedroom to the kitchen to the living room of our two-bedroom duplex. I watched black and white reruns of *My Favorite Martian* while I enjoyed an afternoon snack. Sometimes I found myself alone at night too, when my mom was working late shifts as a dispatcher. I called her to quiet my fears and answered quickly when she called to check on me. Eventually, I'd learn to quiet those fears on my own.

I practiced being alone again in my preteen and early teen years when my mother took the two of us away again after the divorce. This time I walked home, quietly consumed in my thoughts. Alone. Once again, I found an empty house. Snacks and television were my friend and distraction—a way to numb myself from all the alone I felt inside.

When I was thirteen and my step-mom kicked me out of the house at Christmas, without a word of explanation, I made an unconscious shift. It eliminated the discomfort of isolation and made a home of it. I learned then that my only true source of comfort was in being alone. I was myself there, not like the way I pretended to be around others. That was so exhausting. When I was alone, there were no explanations, no pretending to be okay, no faking. I already knew the truth.

I left the wild behind, almost forgetting it was there at all, and I began the work of scaffolding a new self around the old one I thought I knew. I wasn't able to hide the truth from myself like I could from everyone else. Not yet. I just built a new place I went to feel comfortable. A place I could be honest about my reality or numb myself from it, the only place I felt comfortable being myself.

My new home was, alone.

Alone: He Wasn't There

"...children have a 'hole in their soul' in the shape of their dads and if fathers are unable or unwilling to connect with them physically, emotionally and spiritually, it can leave a wound that is not easily healed." - Roland C. Warren

I grew up with a soft-hearted dad. He grew up around hunters and hunting but couldn't bring himself to shoot an animal for sport or for meat. He was so soft-hearted about animals that the few times I saw him brought to tears, an animal was usually involved—kittens that crawled up in the motor of our car for warmth and didn't survive when it was turned on to leave for work. Dad tried to bury them quietly before anyone else awoke, but I noticed the soft spot in the ground when I couldn't find the kittens. By the time he arrived home after work, I had an idea that was confirmed by the tears he was trying to hide.

Again I saw those tears when we rode to town together and a family of opossums crossed the road in front of us. Hitting the mother and her two babies was unavoidable, but the pain of hurting the small family of animals was too much to bear. He did not shake it easily.

He was the kind of dad that had a hard time saying no. When my brother or I heard no from our mother, we knew that a yes wasn't too far away if we were devious enough to ask our pushover dad. We played that trick many more times than we should have.

My dad was the one that made all of my friends laugh when they came over to play or stay the night. He jumped on the trampoline with us, embarrassing me by making funny faces and sending his knees flying high into the air. He teased my friends, trying to make them laugh. I acted like I didn't like it. I was never afraid to bring my friends to my house then. There was nothing to hide or fear.

My older brother was always there, too. Our relationship was typical of siblings with a three-year spread. At times he was protector, looking out for his silly, little sister, playing the role of the older, wiser brother. Sometimes he was my babysitter. He was my friend too, my first friend. I gladly played whatever he invited me in on, and he did his best to be patient with me when I tore up his toys or did things the wrong way. Sometimes we wrestled and played rough. I always had tears right near the surface, ready for any chance of things going too far. He was very good at the phrases,

"Are you okay?"

"Please, don't tell mom."

"I'm sorry!"

"Please stop crying."

"I'm sorry."

As we got older, I grew into the role of the tag-along sister that bothered my brother and his friends when they did not want me around. They wanted to do whatever it is that older, preteen boys like to do, without little girls. I tried my best to be a boy to fit in.

They were taken from me—my dad and my brother—when my mom drove away in that little white car that day with me in the passenger seat. There would be no more built-in playmate living in the room next to mine, no one to bother after school or on weekends, no one to give me all of his junk after he meticulously cleaned out his closet or organized his room. He was left behind, leaving only an empty, quiet apartment in his place.

There was no soft-hearted, pushover, goofball of a dad in that apartment either. He was soon replaced with a controlling, angry, younger man who couldn't hold his liquor and never really tried.

The devastation of these losses sank in slowly and quietly. I did not fight, kicking and screaming, to get them back. There were other people, with other needs. They were bigger and louder and more important than mine. I learned to fade into the background to camouflage myself, to need less, want less, ask for little. That was the new way of living, surviving.

Our nights at home together, eating dinner or playing games or watching a movie, were replaced. Now they were nights out while I was home alone, my mom and step-dad returning late and drunk. I learned to be in my room with the door closed, pretending I was asleep to avoid the discomfort they carried through the door with them.

My dad, my brother, they weren't there to see.

The afternoons spent playing with friends at my house and the weekend sleep-overs while my dad made us laugh left my life when my mom and I left that little town. They weren't replaced. I found a new friend in the city, Ruth. I spent many nights at her house, avoiding my own. I learned not to invite friends over. There was so much to hide.

My dad and my brother couldn't be found.

I understood that money was scarce now. There were fewer and fewer shopping trips. My body grew into a womanly shape while my mom shrank herself physically and otherwise. We were nearly the same size, so we shared clothes to save money. My mom looked "young for her age." She was attractive and fit. Secretly, I hated that. I wished for a mom that was older, bigger, matronly, one who packed school lunches with little notes inside and had cookies waiting when I got home. I wished for a mom, a family, like the ones I saw on TV I didn't want a mom that turned men's heads or wore the same size as her thirteen-year-old daughter.

Still, my dad was not there. My brother was gone.

I soon realized that there always seemed to be enough money for beer in the fridge or vodka in the freezer. Things previously considered necessities, became more and more scarce as time went on, everything was second to alcohol. I could have gone to my mom to ask for what I needed, talk about what I was feeling, or complain. I knew that she would sob and apologize and worry about all the ways she was failing the daughter she loved. My mom was now a victim of so many circumstances in her life, each one added stress pushing her farther and farther to an edge I feared seeing the other side of. So, I learned to be quiet—not complain and ask for little. I ate only things like tuna and cereal and Raman noodles. These things, I'd learned from a friend's older sister, were cheap and helped you lose weight. I could control that—one of the few things I could control. The shrinking inside eventually led to shrinking outside. I became a shell, thin with dark circles under my eyes.

And still they weren't there—my brother, my dad.

I missed my brother, but I'd learn to forget that too—to leave the memories of the connection we had to the wild and to each other behind. That was how I survived.

I survived in the best way I knew how, at eleven and twelve and thirteen and fourteen, I survived. I developed unconscious and misinformed coping skills that made me easy-going and likable and pretty. They made me appear fine on the outside. I even tricked myself into believing it too, sometimes. Most people wouldn't see the inside—what was really going on—while distracted with the outside.

But there was one, one who saw, one who looked deeper. Or maybe it was her parents who noticed, and knew better. Maybe they saw past that feeble facade I constructed over the pain beneath. They took me in. They packed me up in their car, took me back to that tiny town, and moved me into their basement. They asked nothing of me. They let me be, let me live.

My dad did not know. He did not see. He was not there.

City: Rescue

"Vulnerability is the core of shame and fear and our struggle for worthiness, but it appears it's also the birthplace of joy, of creativity, of belonging, of love." - Brené Brown, TEDxHouston: The Power of Vulnerability

There are rare, remarkable, unforgettable moments of salvation that, one can only hope, happen for all of us. When we're lost in the weeds of trauma, where the mere act of survival takes nearly all, if not all, of one's energy and attention, these moments must be hard to see. From a more advantaged view—one where safety, love, support, and encouragement are without question—from that place saving graces are easier to see. This was not the case for my thirteen-year-old self. My view then was from one of the deepest and darkest depths I might ever find myself. From there, my salvation would have to get right up close, look me directly in the eyes, and spell it out slowly.

My second intervention was like that. It took place in a Wendy's booth in Pueblo, Colorado, the city. At least it felt like an intervention. My mom, Dan, and I had been living in a house across town, our third place together since moving to that city—an old,dingy, single-story house. It wasn't a better neighborhood, just a different one. The discounted rent from Dan's brother, our landlord, was the deciding factor for the move.

It was a distance from my school, so now I required rides for the twenty-minute commute at the end of my eighth-grade year. This allowed me to attend the same middle school I'd gone to since sixth grade. The same middle school where I'd witnessed hallway drug deals and schoolyard fights, huffed marker fumes before class; the same middle school that held the round table in the little, white room where my first intervention was staged.

This house, across town, was closer to the church I attended so regularly that I had decided to get baptized there. I wasn't alone at church on that Sunday. My grandparents attended, my mom, maybe my dad and step-parents. I can't really remember. It was a blur. The blurriness may have been a result of being submerged in the baptism pool in front of the large congregation of Baptists. I agreed to it thinking it would wash away all that dirt I had been carrying around inside. It was getting heavy after three years. It didn't work. Even a baptism couldn't wash me clean.

Maybe the events of that time were a bit blurry because I found myself fully submerged in withdrawal, another effort at survival. My eighth-grade year at a close, I spent hours alone walking around and around the trapezoid-shaped park across the street from our house while listening to tapes on my Walkman, songs like Harry Chapin's *Cat's in the Cradle* on repeat. The rest of my hours were spent alone, too, filled with getting lost in television, then lost in books behind a closed bedroom door as soon as my mom and step-dad came home.

Could he be called a step-dad? Can you call someone, whose only glances in my direction held all the disdain he could muster, Dad? Surely, he hoped that if he ignored my existence long enough, I might actually disappear. This was the same treatment afforded to the mice around our house—just ignore them long enough and they'll go away. I was—a little pest he hoped would leave of its own accord. This tactic wasn't working with the mice, but he'd mastered another strategy to cope with this.

When he drank enough, everything disappeared.

He was right about me. Three years of living with his emotional and alcohol abuse, made me disappear a little more every day. My mom must have been disappearing too because she didn't seem to notice.

Though my real dad moved from Wiley, the small town we lived in before the divorce, I maintained some sincere friendships there. I got an occasional escape by visiting them on weekends. I'd stay with a friend, Kate. I didn't have to disappear at her house. Things weren't as fuzzy there. We smiled and laughed and did silly thirteen-year-old things together before I went back home, two hours away. Only once, I let Kate into my world enough to invite her to stay the weekend with me.

That weekend, we walked to a used record store, buying old records. Anything with a catchy title or interesting album cover ended up in our bag. Records like the *Fame* soundtrack with songs like *Hot Lunch* and *Adam Ant's* record with *Never Trust a Man (With Egg on His Face)* were our favorites. We found a candy store, where we loaded up on bags of sugary treats by the scoopful and handfuls of pastel-colored taffy wrapped in wax paper. We walked around the park together then, talking and laughing as we went. I don't know what Kate saw when she stayed with me that weekend. To me, it was the best weekend since I moved there.

Kate must have noticed more than she let on. I learned this when we met her dad, who drove the two hours, to pick Kate up at the end of that weekend. We met at the Wendy's down the road. We sat at the brown, slick table in the corner by the window when the intervention began. I was too detached, too fully wrapped up inside myself, to cry as I heard my best friend's dad begin.

"Do you want to go to high school here?" he was asking.

I noticed how nicely his full, gray-white beard and trimmed, gray-white hair went with his corduroy pants and gingham plaid shirt. If he'd been wearing tweed and smoking a pipe, he'd have been full-on professor, for sure. I thought someone that looked like that must be a real dad, not the kind that drinks to unconsciousness daily or makes you feel like you should somehow shrink yourself to the size of a mouse and disappear into a little hole.

I just stared back at him blankly in answer.

"If you don't want to go to high school here, you can move in with us, and come back to go to school with your friends in Wiley again," he went on.

He must have seen or understood or heard the lists of questions swirling in my mind then. He didn't wait for an answer. He just went on.

"Kate and her mom are okay with it. They want you to stay with us if you'd like to," he said. He wasn't pleading or emotional, just calmly stating facts. Everything about him showed that he was whole on his own. He didn't need me to agree to his proposal to make himself feel better. He just knew where I might find a bit of solace in the storm of my life. He knew a place I might find a little hope.

I did cry then, maybe imagining being somewhere that felt light, without the weight of the shame and secrets and fear. It might have been the thought of being somewhere that someone might actually want me to be. It was most certainly the idea that I might be allowed to be somewhere that I wanted to be, somewhere for me.

And as quick as those thoughts were allowed to enter my mind, they were gone. Guilt and fear and worry and blame entering and filling up the space of hope.

"What about my mom?" I thought aloud. Who would take care of her? Who would listen to her cry on the weekends after she'd had too much to drink and could let all of her fears and worries out? Who would be there for her, a voice of reason or a strong shoulder to help her through her days? What would happen to her?

"Sometimes, Debbie, it's okay to be selfish," he said. And those words took flight right across the table and landed in my heart and in my soul and would never leave. I took comfort in them over and over again, though never really believing them or understanding their meaning until years later.

"Really?" I asked of this new revelation. "Really?" Being selfish was an affront to my whole existence and everything I'd been taught, by my family, my church, and the actions of those closest to me.

"Yes, Debbie. Really," he answered.

With that permission, I found my first small steps to freedom, for a little while.

Alone: Christmas

"Traumatized people chronically feel unsafe inside their bodies: the past is alive in the form of gnawing interior discomfort. Their bodies are constantly bombarded by visceral warning signs, and, in an attempt to control these processes, they often become experts at ignoring their gut feelings and in numbing awareness of what is played out inside. They learn to hide from themselves." - Bessel A. Van Der Kolk, The Body Keeps the Score

I learned to hate Christmas that year, the year my brother drove the hour to pick me up at Kate's home in Wiley, where I had lived for the past six months, during the beginning of my freshman year of high school. It was night, dark, and snowing—a typical Colorado winter storm. Not the kind of weather or roads intended for us or the little, gold, two-door Nissan Pulsar my brother drove. Barely seventeen, he now lived in the basement of my aunt and uncle's house on the ranch, the wild place we'd called home what felt like a lifetime ago. We'd both lived many lives since then.

Though he was unhappy about this trip we were guilted into, he drove the three and a half hours on Christmas Eve to the apartment our mother moved to with our step-dad—still *Dan*—anyway. His anger seeped out of him as he drove through the storm, gangster rap blasting from over-sized speakers that filled the trunk. I told him, annoyed, that I didn't think this was appropriate Christmas Eve music. This did not make things better. He turned up the volume. We did not talk.

We arrived late at night. Late enough to go to bed, but *Dan* wasn't ready for bed yet. I knew the type of person Dan was by then. He was a person who existed only in rooms where his perceived needs became the needs of everyone else in the room. Everyone else's needs became secondary or were forgotten altogether.

The alcohol he drank before we got there made him welcoming. I learned to be cautious of this version of Dan. It was hard to tell if this was an effort for him or if he simply drank so much waiting for us to arrive that he thought he would try being fun and entertaining. Despite his efforts and my mother's, the loneliness of that holiday was palpable to anyone that hadn't been drinking all day to numb it away.

Dan kept us awake, the living room being the only place for my brother and me to sleep in their one-bedroom apartment—the place she lived without us, her seventeen and fourteen-year-old children—the children seeing for the first time where she now lived; the children that didn't know if their step-dad even had a job let alone what the day-to-day lives of him and our mother entailed. The three of us, our mom and my brother and myself, were so far removed from each other now that being together was more than uncomfortable. We just sat and watched the spectacle that was *Dan.* He waited until midnight. That's when the real fun began.

I didn't know what the argument was about, I could barely hear it coming from down the hall. Mom's hushed tone sounded forced and angry while my step-dad, moving his body and his mouth in that drunk way, gave my mom's unease away. All of us knew how this argument would end, my mom included, how any argument with the force that was *Dan* would end. He would do or get or say or act exactly as he chose or wanted, while those around him compensated for this in whatever way required. The world in his immediate radius would revolve around any dysfunction he decided to bless it with.

When he broke free from my mom and into the living room that barely fit the over-sized couch and love seat my brother and I sat on, I saw the cause of the argument. In his right hand, Dan held a small, black pistol. In a one-bedroom apartment with limited square footage, there was no room left for the weight that pistol wielded about. The heaviness of all that was unspoken already filling the corners and nooks and crannies—the shame, the fear, the uncertainty, the guilt. A pistol in the hands of an alcoholic that had consumed far more drink than even he typically handled should incite panic. Yet, there was no panic found in his expression or actions or words. The alcohol in his system had long since numbed any of that. The rest of us in the room, we were much too desensitized to circumstances like this to be reactive either.

In these instances, when a typical fear response should take over, where most people would yell or cry or run or do *something, anything*—a different reaction took over our bodies. People repeatedly exposed to actions and behaviors that activate the nervous system's fight or flight response become desensitized to this chemical overload in their body. Humans, big and small, repeatedly traumatized—told and shown that they are unsafe or whose basic needs are consistently unmet—forget to run or fight. They learn to shut down, to cope, to minimize the amount of damage that will be done rather than avoid it or eliminate it.

As Dan began waving the pistol about yelling and laughing like he was impressing my seventeen-year-old brother, the three of us began to withdraw. Our bodies and our actions showed that we were, in fact, desensitized to such behavior. We got quiet. We became calm. We may have even feigned weak laughter in an attempt to go with the flow and not make things worse by resisting.

My brother stepped in. I don't know if he'd been drinking too, though there's no doubt that drink was offered to him in an attempt at connection or solidarity. It didn't matter. He skillfully got the belligerent body that had sucked up all the air in the room outside. The two of them went out the front door together, while my mom and I stayed still in the small living room full of furniture. We didn't talk. We didn't even go outside to protect or save my brother. The only movement from inside would be the long, slow release of air that we'd been holding in our lungs. From outside came a whooping and hollering, a cheer, and then a shot, a fire that rang out from the pistol, then another.

Neither of us yelled or cried or screamed or even ran outside to assess the situation. I slowly and quietly made my way to the window to peek out through the mini blinds that blocked our view. I saw the man that I was supposed to call step-dad, outside in the middle of the road, in his skin-tight, white tank top meant as an undershirt and his equally tight shorts, holding that gun straight up in the air as my brother walked back to the door shaking his head. I looked back at my mom, no words exchanged between us.

The three of us sat in silence as Dan staggered back inside and through the hall to the bedroom in the back. We sat there until the police arrived to check on the disturbance. My mom did what she'd gotten so good at doing over the past four years that *Dan* had been in her life, excusing and explaining away his behavior. She buffered and cushioned all the damage he left in his wake.

My brother and I were grateful to get what little sleep we did on the couches in the front room that night. We woke early the next morning, left as soon as we could free ourselves of the weight of that place and the people that brought us there. We said hushed goodbyes to our mother while Dan slept it off in the bedroom. Then we drove three and a half hours back to where I was living, never saying a word to each other about what happened. I didn't say anything about rap music playing loudly in the car now. My brother dropped me off then took himself to the separate place he called home, and the two of us never mentioned a word of it again—to each other, to our mom, or to anyone else. This was my normal. This was how I knew to survive—shutting down, shutting up, covering up, hiding, ignoring, denying. The darkness I hid it all under unknowingly became the breeding ground for massive amounts of shame I carried with me for decades.

I didn't see my dad that Christmas. Phoenix, Arizona where he now lived with my step-mom was too far to drive in one day, and I wasn't sure that my brother and I had been invited. We spent the many holidays that followed however, driving from one parent to the other, wherever our parents happened to be living that year. My brother and I bounced from one to the other to do what we thought pleased our parents.

When I was old enough to drive and had a car of my own, I made the drive alone. I spent Christmas Eve in one place and Christmas day hours away in another, still trying to make everyone happy. But no one was, not really. It would go on this way for years, trying to please everyone and pleasing no one at all, eventually reducing Christmas to a dreaded time of year, every year. I found no joy in this holiday, but I hid that away too. No one knew, not even me.

Alone: A Mother Again

"And here is the thing we must know about our things if we are ever going to survive them: we believe we can bury them, when the truth is, they are burying us. They will always bury us, eventually." - Laura McKowen, We Are the Luckiest

My mom made her way back to me again. She found a way to leave Dan—that man that made trauma, fear, and lack a part of our everyday lives. Maybe that last Christmas was one of many last straws added to a pile that finally toppled down. Maybe it was being without either of her children for the last year of her life. Maybe it was those things, but I suspected it was something else. I thought maybe it was what went on behind closed doors when no one else was around that my mom couldn't take any longer. Maybe, I thought, the fear and uncertainty, the down-right distaste I felt being in the same room as Dan, was nothing compared to the fear my mom felt in his presence. What else would make a woman give up so much—her friends, her children, any familiarity of life she once knew—for such a person?

After I moved out of my mom's house and in with my friend Kate's family, my mom gained enough strength and courage to take a small bit of her life back. She worked diligently to get a good job—secure, with benefits, and a decent salary. Somehow, Mom found the courage to use this job offer as an ultimatum, she would move to Alamosa, Colorado as the job required, with or without Dan. He moved with her then, two hours south of Pueblo, the town he'd grown up and lived in his entire life, rather than lose my mom or the sense of control being with her gave him. My mom worked there, to support herself and Dan, the only paycheck to pay for his daily trips to the liquor store, as far as I knew.

When the police became involved, the night Dan fired the pistol in the street, the small pieces of strength and freedom my mom was able to grasp looked like they may slip through her hands again. Now *she* was given an ultimatum by her boss: see a therapist (to her fortune, her boss identified the codependency that was holding her down) or lose her job. This ultimatum and the subsequent therapist gifted her the smallest bits of courage and self-worth, enough to leave her second husband, transfer her position to a town much closer to me, and move into a house with me, just a couple of blocks down the same street I lived on in Kate's house. This would be my fifteenth address.

My mom and I lived in this two-bedroom rental house together. My brother didn't trust our mom enough to move back in with her yet, but we did our best to make it a home. We painted the walls and decorated the rooms. We had guests over and we laughed and ate together again. Air filled the rooms again and there was a lightness in our days. We talked, but not really. We never talked about what happened between us or how we felt or what we wanted. We just went on living in that house down the road from the family who fostered me when things got too bad to bear, as if nothing like that had happened at all.

I saw Dan one last time. He came for a weekend visit. He was on his best behavior. He still drank, I knew, but I did my best to stay away from him and he did the same. I was old enough and comfortable enough, back in this small, wild town, to come and go as I pleased. I'd learned to take care of myself now. The thought of him visiting made me feel sick to my stomach. The thought of him being in the little house we spent summer evenings painting a fresh, pure white, made me want to lock the door and not let him in. Instead, I ran away when he came, made myself busy with friends and stayed at their houses. My face crinkled in disgust at the thought of seeing my mom dress nice and make herself up, wear a fake personality, and use a fake voice for Dan. I felt nauseous just thinking of my mom changing herself to please this man that had changed us all in ways from which we'd never recover. So now I left, closed the door behind me and forgot it all away.

I never talked to her about it. I never told her how I felt—as though he shook up my whole life like a snow globe then dropped it on the floor, tiny, broken pieces shattering in all directions, and then walked away. That wasn't my job anymore. My job, I thought, was to be the one that forgave without ever being asked. My job was to move on and move forward. I took on the responsibility so quietly that others might not have noticed this change in me, not even my own mother. I wore these skills as naturally as the skin I was born in. I became so skilled at it all—forgetting, forgiving, moving on, mothering—that even I began to believe it was just who I was.

Alone: Rescue Two

"But people are oceans…You cannot know them by their surface." - Beau Taplin, Surfaces

Things went on this way for all of that year—my mom and I living together, in denial, as if nothing had happened, *happily ever after*—until they didn't.

Dan was finally out of the picture, for good. Somehow, their divorce finalized, and we moved on, never discussing how or when or why it happened. I didn't care, and I definitely didn't want to do anything to jeopardize the stability I felt now. I knew that.

There were other men. My mom mentioned them. They came to pick her up, or I occasionally came home to find them in the living room or kitchen talking. Mostly, she separated them from me now, and I was relieved. I feared that even including them in our conversation might be the first, simplest act of inviting them into my life, as though even whispering about it would somehow recreate the past. I did not want to invite any more men of my mom's choosing into my life.

Things did change, even when we didn't talk about it. Eventually, my mom was required to relocate in order to keep her stable job. This time she found an apartment in Ft. Collins, Colorado, hours away again. Maybe I should have gone with her. Maybe. There was never much discussion. I told my mom I wasn't moving, the fear of what happened when we moved away together the previous time not yet a distant memory. My mom, holding the same memory, did not argue or force me to move with her. She rationalized that it wouldn't be fair to ask me to change schools my junior year of high school. We separated again.

This time, I lived in the basement of another friend's house, Lillie. I feared myself being too much of a burden to move back in with Kate's family a second time, and Lillie's older sister was moving out to attend college in Nebraska. My mom moved over four hours away into an apartment by herself while I crashed in a friend's basement. I went to school during the day, then drove to work as a discount store clerk afterward. Lillie's mom often saved a plate of dinner for me for when I got home. On nights I didn't work, we all sat together at the table, eating like a real family.

I had only two friends then, that truly knew my story, both friends who helped me make their basements a temporary home. I was a cheerleader and a girlfriend and a student. I did my homework and got good grades. I smiled and answered, "Good," if ever I was asked about how I was doing. No one knew the truth, not really, only me. My two best friends also mostly knew, but we never talked about it—the pain, the loneliness, the truth.

Alone: Another One

"Yet all too often, guilt is just another name for impotence, for defensiveness destructive of communication; it becomes a device to protect ignorance and the continuation of things the way they are, the ultimate protection for changelessness." - Audre Lorde, Sister Outsider

My mom met another man, this one brought her back to me once more. She quit her job and moved back to town, for him, after a surprise pregnancy. I moved out of the basement bedroom in Lilly's house, where I'd been living for the previous year.

At the end of the summer before my senior year of high school, I loaded all of my possessions into the back hatch of the little, gold car—the one I borrowed from my brother. It took me to and from school each day, then to and from work each night. I cracked the window as I lit my cigarette on the way "home," watching the red-orange glow of the cherry colored ash at the end. It glowed brighter with each deep inhale. Each cigarette had become a friend.

Now, I took my few things to another tiny, two-bedroom apartment I shared with my mom and her new boyfriend, Ken. I fit fine. I didn't need much space.

I borrowed my mom's car now. The same one that took us away from home years before, from my dad and my brother, all those years ago. I drove that car to clean houses with a friend's mom each morning, then to my other job each afternoon. I left sports and cheerleading behind.

Ken and my mom quickly married, shotgun style, and we found a different house to rent, one with more space, and an extra bedroom for my little sister that was soon to arrive. I once again found refuge in a room in the corner of the basement. Quickly, I realized what my mom couldn't or didn't want to see—she'd found a different version of the same mistake she'd left behind not so long ago.

I watched as entire cases of beer entered the house and left in the trash can almost daily. I noticed Ken crack one open as soon as he got home from work, teaching high school shop, and continue drinking until late in the night when he passed out in bed. It was easier to ignore the second time around. My mom's belly rounding with the daughter inside made her blind to many things. My new step-dad made it easier for us both, too. Unlike his predecessor, he remained surprisingly functional. He drove to work every day without fail, whether he was green with a hangover or even a little wobbly from the alcohol still in his system. This dad did not look at me like I was filth. He did not consume the house with his own selfishness, entitlement, anger, control, and abuse like the one I had before.

Ken was unpredictable in his highs and lows. He spent too much of the money they didn't have on beer. Those things were familiar. But he did not have the same darkness seeping from him and consuming everything he touched, like Dan had. My new step-dad was much younger than my mom, so part of his drinking was blamed on his age. The rest of it was forgotten by his occasional kindness and attempts at connection with both my mom and me. When you're dying of thirst, even the tiniest puddle looks like an ocean.

Ken's drinking affected me much less this time around. I knew better how to pretend it away. I was older now too. At seventeen, I filled most of my days with school, work, and friends, not getting home until after dinner most nights. I made sure to be home as little as possible. After my sister was born, it was even easier to stay out late. I went to parties with my older boyfriend on the weekends, getting my own taste for alcohol now. As long as I didn't wake the sleeping baby and my tired mother, I could return at any time before the sun rose. My older boyfriend, out of high school, stayed over without anyone knowing. He sneaked out before the sun rose.

I applied to a state college in the same town that my boyfriend lived. I kept my aim low, making sure it was a place I wouldn't be denied and controlling what little I could by keeping the uncertainties of taking risks and striving for more at bay. Ken helped me apply for financial aid, that and student loans made it possible to attend college in the town four hours away. I found my way out now, the safest, most predictable way a seventeen-year-old girl could find. I would not fail, could not. I would keep my expectations and efforts low enough to ensure that—the only way out of this undesirable cycle I could see.

Perfect: Drug Of Choice

"Chronic people-pleasing is a survival mechanism that develops when a child's expression of emotions results in temporary removal from a parent's love. The child learns that sharing their emotions poses a threat to their safety and belonging, so they learn to suppress their own needs as a means for survival." - Kate Lally

I ran. I tried to avoid all of the things I feared becoming by running away from them and denying they existed. I built a life around being so afraid of becoming my mother that I lost the core of myself in the process. I made major life decisions from a place fear—fear of being a bad person, fear of not being liked, fear of turning out just like my mom. My mom told me so many times, "History repeats itself." Well, I would do my best to make sure it didn't. I was so afraid of becoming my mother, that every conscious action I took, though there were few, was in direct opposition to what I thought she might have done.

Example one: though my mom was fully capable and admirably intelligent, she had never completed her college degree. I heard her talk about her desire to be an occupational therapist frequently. Something always got in the way of making it happen—money, time, other people's needs. The only light at the end of the tunnel I saw, my only way out, was to create a new life by getting a college degree. From my limited view, it was the only path I knew that might lead away from alcoholism, helplessness, poverty, and codependency. Going away to college was a temporary denial of the life I was fleeing, but it was also the first step to building a life I hoped would take me out of the one I had grown to hate, toward predictability and stability.

This was not a graceful path. I had not yet found my drug of choice to numb away the life I wanted so much to forget. College provided a platform to try many out. There were nights full of drinking away the pain and the insignificance I felt deep inside. The alcohol found its way past my insecurity and inhibitions, took down my walls, and gave me a false sense of freedom and joy and confidence. It opened me up to the advances of boys around me and allowed me to settle for those that were most persistent, in closest proximity, or were also feeling the effects of alcohol. Those moments gave me a false sense of self-worth and glossed over my insecurities through feeling wanted by someone. Relaxing my inhibitions with alcohol lead to trying my hand, a handful of times, at light drugs. Those would not become my numbing form of choice. I settled on things like booze, and boys, and food, and television, in an acceptable alternating fashion. The guise of college allowed my repeated, drunken nights to appear socially appropriate.

The boys and booze made me forget my lack only until the following morning. I spent those waking hours combing through my vague memories (sometimes none) of the night before, compiling a list of regrets. They eventually settled in a cloud of shame that only added to the pain and fear I was trying so desperately to forget. Desperate—a good word for the feeling I was building inside, the person I was becoming.

I allowed none of these things to get in the way of my way out, however—my degree. I earned that, in spite of all my misguided choices. I walked across the stage, clasped that diploma against my chest—my family watching, all of them—and found solace in the first guarantee I had that I'd not become my mother.

Leaving college behind, allowed me to leave the drunken haze of bad decisions behind as well. I shoved that shame atop my growing pile, like compacted trash in a bag that needs to be taken out. There I could pretend it never happened at all.

Leaving boys and booze behind, so many shameful nights teaching me those things didn't numb the pain but only added to it. After college, I began numbing my pain in a different way. I started perfecting my outsides, words, and actions, sculpting myself, superficially, into what I thought would please those around me. Now I found validation and worth in becoming what I thought others might want me to be. This way of numbing felt much better, much more in my control—controlling the perceptions of others by over-controlling myself. There was nothing shameful in that.

—

I found a partner I unconsciously knew could fill all the holes I felt inside, making me feel more seamless from the outside. We were old friends, having graduated high school together, and seemingly knew each other well. Eventually, we'd settle on moving back to the rural area we'd grown up in and our family still lived—all safe choices. Together we did things in the correct, socially acceptable order—college degrees, dependable jobs with pensions, marriage, buy the house with the white picket fence and then kids. This was not the order my mom chose, so this must be better.

As time went on, I found ways to continually perfect my appearance—my hair, my clothes, my make-up, my body. This process would take years, but I was committed to making myself *look* perfect.

People really liked it when I worked hard, too. I learned to show up early and leave late. I took on many projects and used the word 'yes' a lot.

"Okay," I'd say. "I can do that."

And I would, trying as often as I could to exceed expectations. People liked that too. It would take years to become a perfect co-worker, a perfect teacher. I committed to that too. I got better at making people like me. This felt much better than shame-filled mornings punctuated with a hangover. It numbed my past and my insides away so much better. It was much more socially acceptable. The only thing I had to hide now, was my past, the years of guilt and shame and dirt I'd been stuffing deep inside. It was much easier to do that when the outside always appeared so perfectly perfect.

Having kids added to the opportunities for perfection. I painted and decorated my daughters' rooms until they looked just right. Then got lost in being the perfect mom, doing everything just as the books said, as society expected. This would surely produce the perfect child, dressed in the cutest clothes, that everyone loved, to build upon all the perfect I was getting so good at. It would take years to be the perfect mother. I kept at it.

Little by little, I found my drugs of choice—perfectionism and people-pleasing. There couldn't be a better cover. Building a beautiful facade around the crumbling walls I held within gave me everything I thought I needed. It allowed me to forget where I'd come from, where I'd been, all the hurt and pain I'd seen and experienced, finding a new sense of worth in being what I thought everyone else wanted me to be, what I wanted to be—perfect.

As I became better and better at perfecting myself by becoming what I thought others wanted and needed, by doing for others as much as I could, I became more and more lost to myself. I lost the pain, the struggle, the shame, the regrets. I could almost forget they existed. But this meant I also lost so many pieces that made me who I was. I lost any ability to take risks and grow and stand out, for fear of failing, of not being perfect. Perfecting and people-pleasing took away the pain. They made me feel better. Until, like all drugs, one day they didn't.

Perfect: Seeking Permission

"What kills a soul? Exhaustion, secret keeping, image management. And what brings a soul back from the dead? Honesty, connection, grace." - Shauna Niequist, Present Over Perfect

I knew something was wrong, deep within. I could feel it seeping out of me, almost as if it was coming from my innermost core, my marrow. It just kept coming, leaking from the sticky edges of the bandages covering all the cracks. They weren't working anymore. I knew it. Maybe no one else noticed, yet, but I knew I needed to take care of it soon or they would.

My search for a diagnosis began. It wasn't enough at this point to know that something was wrong. I needed validation and approval—permission—from an expert. I wanted a metaphorical slip I could take to my husband, my boss, my parents, or my mother-in-law—something to prove that something was wrong with me, that I was broken, physically. I couldn't just say to them,

"I'm tired. I'm in pain. I need a break. I need some rest."

Who was *I* to decide that for myself?

But if a real doctor could say that there was really something wrong with me, maybe it would be okay to stop for a moment. Maybe, a doctor would tell me it was time to slow down. Maybe, a doctor would give me permission to take care of myself for a while. Then I could tell the people in my life I needed a break, without letting them down. Then I could take a break while still keeping the illusion of all the layers of perfect I had built up around myself.

—

Health problems continued to present themselves after the initial diagnoses (rheumatoid arthritis, mixed-connective tissue disease, Raynaud's so severe in my toes that they swelled from "frost-bite" until they cracked open and bled each winter). I had plenty of those now. Not just one or two, but many. I gathered them up like petals and stuck them together into a wilted and crumpled treasure that almost resembled a flower. I carried it around with me, wearing it on the lapel of my self-worth.

It turned out I didn't need a break or to stop, while hopped up on external validation and prednisone (a steroid commonly prescribed to people with autoimmune disease). It gave me more than enough energy to keep moving forward. I kept pleasing others and kept building up layers of perfection then. I trusted very few people enough to tell them about my poor physical health. I spoke only of it in hushed conversations with those closest to me. People were really impressed now, the people who knew. I could work full-time, raise a couple of kids, feed a husband, and keep a clean house and tidy appearance, all with autoimmune diseases. Boy, I could do it all!

I learned when the high of the corticosteroid prescription wore off, that all I was left with, again, was myself—the same tired, sick, deeply wounded self I'd been trying so hard to hide.

Perfect: Someday

"The sorrow which has no vent in tears may make other organs weep." - *Henry Maudsley*

This wasn't the first conversation I'd had like this. I didn't have a crystal ball, but I knew it wouldn't be my last. I was sitting on an exam table in a hospital gown, bare legs dangling, my cold arms exposed. They always kept places like this cold. I felt like a child, in the helpless sort of way, small on the inside though I was fully adult on the outside.

Across from me stood a doctor, my doctor, another one. This time it was a pulmonologist. He really was a small man, on the outside that is, surely not on the inside based on his mannerisms and behavior—walking in quickly, speaking in an energetic, friendly, unguarded fashion that was atypical of other specialists I'd seen. Then he too would scroll through the screen on his computer, reading over my chart notes, with me as an audience. He was just the third specialist and fourth doctor I'd seen since seeking answers for the uncharacteristic pain I'd been feeling since I gave birth to my youngest daughter two and a half years earlier.

"So, you're 33 years old?" he asked without looking over from his screen.

"Yes," I replied flatly

"And you've had a positive ANA...Oh! A positive RNP?" his voice a mixture of shock and intrigue at this last point.

That one seemed to get the other doctors, too. I came to realize that what sounded worrisome and hard to understand in my lab results, was what most excited my doctors. They tried to mask their excitement, of course, but I heard and felt it every time I became just a little more interesting to them. I would brace myself for the further discoveries I knew were waiting for him as he scrolled.

"It looks like you've been diagnosed with rheumatoid arthritis...with mixed connective tissue disease?" He said this last part with a lifted tone like it was a question.

I didn't answer. I didn't think he was expecting an answer to all of these questions.

"That's very rare," he said, once again failing to mask his excitement.

"Well, I guess I was diagnosed with those things when I went to my first rheumatologist," I answered finally. "But my new rheumatologist, here at National Jewish, has backed off of making those as final diagnoses...I think..." I began to use that questioning tone now also, mirroring him.

"I think that she is maybe just calling it undifferentiated connective tissue disease?" I asked this time.

"Oh, I see that now," he said. "Yes!"

"Yeah, I'm not really super interested in a specific diagnosis," I chimed in. "It sounds like most of these diseases are very similar anyway. I really just want to take care of the pain I'm having and see what I can do to make sure it doesn't come back after that."

"Ok," the little man with the dark ponytail answered as he got up from the computer and walked over to my side at the exam table. I noticed his black dress shoes, with a slightly larger heel than most men wore. His shoes along with the feminine cut of his trousers and button-up shirt were notable. They made him stand out.

"Well, the reason you're here to see me is that your test results show a couple of things," he continued in his cheerful way, much more talkative than the others. "It looks like you have severe collapse in your trachea and bronchi."

"I guess...The pulmonologist who did the bronchocsopy told my mom that I would need to have some special lung surgery to place stents in my lungs because of that collapse," I answered. "I was still under anesthesia and a little out of it, but I told him I'd just been for a six-mile run the day before." I laughed an uncomfortable laugh as I said it. "He might not have believed me, because I was out of it. It's true, though. I did go for a long run the day before."

"Anyway," I went on, "it was probably more like four miles, but still. Someone who can run four miles shouldn't need stents in their lungs should they?"

Maybe the way I was going on and on showed him the sense of fear I was trying to hide, because he answered back, "Now, don't worry."

There it was, "Don't worry." Was it possible to say anything that might worry someone more than those two words?

"We won't do anything that you don't need. I'll order an exercise tolerance test, and we'll decide where to go from there."

"An exercise tolerance test?" I was trying to ask in a way that implied I was exasperated by the number of tests and that I'd be subject to yet another one.

"It's actually pretty cool!" There was the misplaced excitement again. "We do them right here in house! You'll go upstairs. They'll put you on a bike while you wear a mask and have an IV set up. We'll measure your oxygen output and draw blood throughout to see how your body is responding as you exercise. It's nothing to be afraid of." He tried to convince me in a reassuring tone.

"So, I can do it today?" I asked.

"Oh no, I doubt it. You'll have to schedule it, most likely."

There it was. Another three-hour drive to Denver for another test.

"Have you ever been in a serious accident?" He began a new line of questioning. "Something that would have caused trauma to your chest area, like a car accident or something?"

"No... not that I can think of...not that I remember," the lack of confidence in my tone showed my confusion at this pivot in the conversation.

"Oh, you'd know and remember if something like this had happened to you. It's just that this kind of damage to the cartilage in your lungs," his voice trailed off as he made his way to the computer to have another peek. "The 85 to 95% collapse of the cartilage in your lungs," he continued, "can only be caused by a few things. That makes it easier to narrow down at least…Severe acid reflux that goes into your lungs…" He held up one finger. "Which we ruled out with the acid test we did."

I nodded as I recalled having a small thin tube fed through my left nostril, bringing tears to my eyes. Then severe pain as it apparently got stuck in masses of scar tissue. Only to have it pulled back out and fed through the right nostril, apparently free of such scar tissue, as it was able to pass all the way down through my throat. The worst part had been going into work that morning, after the insertion, to teach a full day of school. I felt obligated not to take time off. My administrator planned on being out and needed me to fill in. I did so, not wanting to disappoint, tube hanging out of my nose the whole time, kids staring in shock. Then the next morning, just in time to make it to school again, I pulled that same tube out of my esophagus, through my throat, and out my nose, myself. I wouldn't forget that test.

"...so it isn't reflux," he was going on, "and it isn't trauma. That really leaves just one other explanation."

"What's that?" I asked, wondering why he wouldn't just tell me in the first place.

"Something called Relapsing Polychondritis," he went on. "Yes, I think what we'll find as your disease progresses, is that you have a combination of Lupus and Relapsing Polychondritis. It would explain your positive RNP, signaling mixed connective tissue disease, and account for all of our findings and test results."

I sat quietly in shock for some unmeasured, slow-moving amount of time, shock brought on by the generosity of information from this strange doctor, strange in the best of ways. So much about him uncharacteristic; his positive, enthusiastic manner, his atypical physicality, and his sheer lack of observance of the usual tight-lipped expectations of specialists like him. He was quick to say whatever had come to his mind, as though he thought his patient had the right to know his full assessment, without worry of whether I could handle or understand all the information.

Most of the doctors I encountered asked a lot of questions and gave very little in return. They just wrote prescriptions, and I'd been left to Google and deciphering chart notes to understand what their thoughts and intentions were.

So here it was, Lupus and Relapsing Polychondritis, whatever that was. He'd left space in the conversation to let it settle.

"It's an autoimmune disease that attacks cartilage," he said finally, in answer to my silence. "It's really out of the ordinary to see it present itself in the lungs first. Usually, patients get something called saddle nose and floppy ears first."

I pictured those aptly named malformations clearly in my head and made a mental note to Google images of them as soon as I was allowed to bolt from this room. I wasn't so cold anymore.

"You had expressed issues with your ears turning red, swollen, and hot in the past, I have those pictures here," he went on. "Dr. Goldstein put you on a course of prednisone for that inflammation. Did it help?"

"Yes, it did," I remembered fondly.

It had been the first bit of steroid my new rheumatologist prescribed, after taking me off my low dose of them when I transferred my care to her nearly a year and a half before. My new rheumatologist thought that being on prednisone for over a year straight was just too long to be good for anyone's body. Going off steroids also allowed the true course of my disease to rear its ugly head so they, the experts, knew exactly what they were dealing with.

"The inflammation of your ear cartilage is another sign of Relapsing Polychondritis," he was saying those words again. "That, with the pain you feel in your rib cage when you breathe, makes it a pretty obvious connection."

"Hrmmm...I've never heard of that," I began to find my voice again, pushing images of a sunken nose and folded ears to the back of my mind. "Is there anything I can do? I mean, to keep it from happening more or help it get better?" From what I understood, it sounded like I needed all the cartilage I had left in my lungs.

"Well, once it's gone, it's gone," he answered. "You can't rebuild cartilage on your own, but how old are you...thirty-three? Who knows, they may be able to grow brand new lungs for you someday. You're still young."

This statement hit me in the heaviest of ways, but I gave no clue. I wanted him to say even more if he was willing.

"OK, but what can I do to help? I mean, I exercise a lot. I eat healthy food. Is there anything else I can do, or maybe a specific exercise or food that would help?" A bit of desperation seeped out in the tone and pace of my questions.

He was up and headed to the door now, as he turned to answer my last questions. I was still sitting—uncomfortably, vulnerably—atop the padded patient table covered in that slick, white paper. It made crinkling sounds as I turned to meet his eye. He looked down.

"Now, exercising and eating well, those things won't hurt," his voice sounded uncomfortable now, too. "Maybe strengthening the muscles in your chest will even help. Strong muscles could help support a weak rib cage. It certainly won't hurt, but…" he had just delivered the but that would change the rest of my life. "But *eventually...someday...*" he said, holding the doorknob as he left his sentence unfinished.

Then I heard nothing else. He walked out, leaving those words floating through the air as though they weren't heavy at all. He was gone. The room was empty, minus the sad, half-naked sight of me on that ridiculous table. I was left to wonder, left to consider those two words.

Eventually...

Someday...

Perfect: Quitter

"...nothing gives life more purpose than the realization that every moment of consciousness is a precious and fragile gift." - Steven Pinker

When I was twenty-seven, my appendix ruptured. I left work early that day. I went home, smoked a cigarette in a secret hiding place in my backyard, and went to bed feeling nauseous and like something wasn't quite right. I got out of bed one time, to pick up my first daughter, only one-year old at the time, from daycare later that afternoon. She lay in bed with me, watching TV while I agonized beside her the rest of the evening. The next morning, a Saturday, I drove myself to the emergency room. I had lost patience with my daughter for no reason that morning. My husband stared at me in shock and disapproval, helping me see it was time to seek medical help.

I drove myself home, too. The E.R. doc told me that I simply had a bladder infection. I didn't argue. I didn't tell the cop who stopped me on the way home where I'd just been. I have no memory of the reason for being pulled over by the city police. He didn't seem to notice the hospital bracelet on my wrist. I cried in pain at home the rest of that weekend, while my husband played video games and showed outward annoyance, sometimes losing his temper and yelling, over my tears.

The following Monday, he took me to the doctor I had called and begged for an appointment to see. I was no longer able to drive myself or get out of my pajamas. I hadn't eaten since Friday. Eventually (another 48 hours later), the cause of my sickness and pain would be discovered, I would be admitted to the local hospital, and I would have the first of three subsequent surgeries to repair the damage. This was all a reflection of what I couldn't yet see: a complete lack of trust in myself, a failure to stand up for myself for fear of upsetting someone else, a repeated relationship pattern with a spouse I had never taught or expected to value me, his wife.

Over seven years later, I sat in my second rheumatologist's office—second because I left the first at my dad's insistence. The first had me taking seven to nine prescription pills three times a day and, not surprisingly in retrospect, feeling worse rather than better. My dad did the research to find the "best" doctor for my conditions, got the number, and all but forced me to make an appointment.

It was a familiar scene, I sat in the chair beside the computer desk while she looked through the test results and chart notes of my other specialist. She said, "It's too bad you have to work." Though we had several conversations about managing my stress to manage my symptoms, nothing ever stuck like that sentence did. I always felt like doctors were telling me it was "all in my head" when they asked me about stress. This time, that sentence, I would never forget. I began to ask myself, over and over, "Do I *have* to work?"

Months later, standing in the office of the elementary school where I taught (rather, held many roles, proving my inability to use the word no)—reading interventionist, team leader for our specialist team, substitute principal, and instructional coach—I surprised myself with my uncharacteristic irritation at a request. The math interventionist on my team was going on about a professional development opportunity out of town, during an upcoming weekend, and wanted me to go along.

Normally the type of thing I jumped at, even sought out and asked for, was suddenly the last thing I wanted to participate in.

"We'll get a stipend," she said. "We'll get paid for our time," still trying to convince me.

Something clicked then, deep inside my heart and my soul. Connections were made about what *I* valued, what *I* wanted, and what *I* needed. I realized something that had never before occurred to me, and it was so new, so true, that I couldn't keep it from coming right out my mouth.

"I don't need more *money*," I said. "I need more *time*." Let it be noted, this had nothing to do with me being rich or fancy or dripping in diamonds, nothing like that. It was strictly a sudden realization that I valued time more than money, that time was worth *a lot* of money.

I didn't remind her of all the *other* weekends, 4:30 a.m. mornings, late-night arrivals, or weeknight hotel stays, I'd spent at professional development opportunities. She didn't need me to tell her about all the evenings I apologized to my daughters' babysitter for picking them up late due to a meeting that went on longer than expected. She knew.

"No," I said. "I'm not going to do it." That was a first. Her mouth wide, jaw dropped, silent, as I walked out of the office and didn't look back.

That night at home was one of the first real conversations I had with my husband—open, honest, difficult, true. That night, through sobs and a hot-red face, I admitted to him and to myself that I didn't know if I would live to retirement age. If I did live that long, I explained, I honestly didn't know what kind of shape my body would be in. I may not be alive or in any kind of shape to enjoy a retirement I was working so hard for now. We both knew that I worked very hard to become skilled at a career I valued greatly. But we also knew that a major motivation for continuing to take my kids to daycare while I taught other peoples' children rather than take a break to raise my own, was the secure pension I was to receive after decades of service. He didn't remind me that with nearly fourteen years under my belt already, I was well on my way. We both remembered that. I shook and gasped and cried so hard, but I spoke the truth anyway.

"I want to live my life *now*," I told him, as his eyes became red and full of tears too, "not *someday*. I want to spend time with the girls now, while I know I still can."

Our marriage had grown immensely in the years since I first started seeing doctors for debilitating pain and learned that my lungs were so severely damaged that they would most likely require surgical intervention for me to continue breathing. The fear of losing a newfound empathy for the pain he saw me enduring, caused him to show up for me in unprecedented ways. He showed more love for me than ever before, through words and actions. He helped me more than ever before, with the kids, house, and cooking. He made me breakfast every morning before work and held me at night in bed as we worried and grieved together. He was truly there for me in our marriage like I'd never before experienced. But *I never asked* for any of that, never expected it. He just did it.

This time, I sat in front of him, being honest in a way I never had been either, asking for what I wanted. Telling him what I wanted and needed from him. I wanted to quit my job and stay home with our daughters, while he supported us financially. That's what I'd do, what we'd do. I'd leave my job and everything would be better. I would be better.

Perfect: Breakthrough

"Until you make the unconscious conscious, it will direct your life and you will call it fate." - Carl Jung

We were standing in the middle of the street having a lengthy conversation because that's what you can do in a small town, you can have full-on chats or jogs or walk your dog right down the middle of the road. Usually, no one else is using them anyway. The few cars that do can easily use the oncoming lane to go around you, and in the off chance that lane is taken, they'll just slow down and wait. Car horns are rare sounds.

About a year after quitting my teaching career, my neighbor began telling me about a visit her daughter just had with a chiropractor. She had been feeling sick and sore after pushing herself through her twice daily swim practices along with swim meets several days a week. This chiropractor adjusted her, I assumed in the typical fashion, then scolded her for eating too much sugar and recommended she buy an extensive assortment of supplements on her way out the door.

"Oh really? What's her name?" I asked.

I went to a couple of chiropractors locally, and none of them had been able to recommend any specific supplements, nor did they sell them directly out of their office. This piqued my interest after listening to Grain Brain by David Perlmutter in the car on a recent road trip through the mountains. My ears were intent on the doctor's insistence that we'll never heal our bodies if we don't have the correct balance of bacteria in our gut—our second brain according to him. I was ready to try a probiotic supplement at this point. It seemed a much more favorable option than a fecal transplant, the other intervention that did favorably in studies.

"Hmmm...I've never heard of her," I said after she told me the chiropractor's name.

"Yeah. She's good. I think she knows what she's talking about. You just have to sort of tune her out when she tries to get you to buy all those supplements," my neighbor was going on. Her daughter making unpleasant faces behind her at the memory of the green pill she'd been told to chew, not swallow.

"I couldn't chew it," she said in response. "I tried but I almost puked. I had to swallow it."

Our back and forth finally broke after I got the chiropractor's phone number. I probably didn't need to make an appointment, I thought. I'd just find the place, get a good probiotic, and be on my way. The hours spent combing through all the probiotic choices at the natural grocery store and on Amazon left me more confused than before I began. Who could figure out what to take with so many choices anyway? I needed some help. After a call into the office, I learned that I would need to make an appointment for such a question. New plan—get an adjustment from the chiropractor, ask her about probiotics, leave with probiotics in hand, and be healed forever.

Several days later, there I was, in my newly acquired stay-at-home-mom attire, black cropped tights, oversized tank, baseball cap, and a sports bra—workout clothes, though I doubt I'd worked out at all that day. Sitting on the orange, vinyl-covered seat gave me time to think about how I would bring up my request for probiotic recommendations. I was rehearsing it in my head when she walked in.

She was a small, attractive, dark-haired woman in her late fifties, I assumed, thinking she looked young for her age. The next few minutes were spent with the small-town run down.

"Oh, I think I know your husband."

"Oh yeah, your husband and my husband used to..."

"How does he like working for..."

"Oh! That's your daughter? No. I don't know her, but I know her mother-in-law."

It's a lot like six-degrees of Kevin Bacon in a small town, only everyone's related to, or worked with, or worked for, or best friends with someone's distant relative when you go on long enough.

"So, why are you here today?" Now we were getting down to business.

By this time, I had been to more than my fair share of doctor appointments. I knew well to keep this part short and sweet. Answer briefly and get in and out quickly. I wasn't looking to kill a couple of hours I didn't have.

"I was hoping you could recommend a probiotic supplement for me. Do you carry those?" That ought to do it.

"Maybe. Why is it you think you need a probiotic?" She wasn't letting me off that easy.

Let's see, to keep this brief, "I just read a book that said they can be helpful to get the right balance of bacteria, and I'd like to try one."

"Ok, so why do you think you need one?" she questioned, her skeptical tone obvious.

"Well, I thought it might help with my autoimmune disease...diseases...I don't know...It seems like a good idea. It couldn't hurt," I answered in my best just-give-me-the-pills-and-let-me-out-of-here-*lady* tone, though I was starting to ramble and quicken my pace. I think she sensed weakness.

"Tell me about your autoimmune disease...diseases? Tell me about that," she said invitingly as she went in for the kill.

And so it went, my not so eloquent elevator pitch of the past three and a half years of my life distilled into lab results, doctors' diagnoses, and prognosis. She was good. I saw that, as it also began to sink in that she had no intention of letting me out of there quickly. Why hadn't she got me on the adjustment table yet?

"So, it's Lupus, then?" she asked without actually expecting an answer as she walked over to a bookshelf.

That's what she got out of all of that? I remember thinking as she selected a small, hard-backed pastel-colored book from the bottom shelf. It looked like the kind of book you might find in a Hallmark store or the gift section of a pharmacy, something you might give your mom on Mother's Day. The smart-ass in me was thinking, this ought to be interesting.

She stared at me as though she might actually be able to hear what I wasn't saying aloud. Then she started flipping casually through the book. When she came to the page she was looking for, she handed it to me and walked to her stack of notes at the counter beside the sink to my left. As I began reading what was on the page, I suddenly felt very small and very warm. Where was that smart ass now? It was just the self-conscious, insecure voice that was saying, *Don't cry. Don't cry. Don't cry!* She had handed me a page of affirmations. It read something like,

I speak up for myself freely and easily.
I claim my own power.
I love and approve of myself.
I am free and safe.

To the left of that, I could see a heading titled, "**Lupus** (Erythematosus): A giving up. Better to die than stand up for oneself. Anger and punishment."

The tears in my eyes came from the truth I felt in that statement and from the lie I sensed in the affirmations—my unconscious thoughts perhaps glimpsing first signs of daylight. I had spent so many years behaving in a way that communicated, "I give up. It's better to die than to stand up for myself." I certainly hadn't been speaking up for myself, let alone "freely and easily." I was not claiming my power, loving, or approving of myself. Nor would I had to have choked back tears over the words, "I am free and safe," if I believed them to be true. This was just beginning to come to the surface now. Just the softest beginnings of the work that would be done to peel away all of the perfecting, the people-pleasing, the pretending to get to the source of true healing.

I did leave with a bottle of probiotics that day, in a brown paper lunch sack spilling over with other supplements too. She really got me. Maybe my neighbor was right. I would have plenty of time to find out in my weekly return visits with my new chiropractor. I knew not yet if she was a phony or a fraud, but I'd find out if I didn't cancel my appointment out of fear masquerading as skepticism.

Real: Raging

"You're beautiful because you know your own darkness, and still that alone doesn't stop you from finding your own light." - R.M. Drake

"Were you abused?" the chiropractor asked, a little gasp of air escaping quickly from her mouth first.

This third visit to the chiropractor had been particularly trying. I didn't understand what was being done to me. All I knew was that it was making it impossible to keep the weak grasp I thought remained of my self-control. Sitting there, tears running down my face and shaking uncontrollably, as the chiropractor performed some strange combination of muscle testing, tapping, and counting backward aloud signifying ages in my life. Maybe these were supposed to be ages that some sort of perceived trauma happened to me that I was "holding onto" for all these years to follow, unconsciously—what my chiropractor believed may be causing the remaining pain in my shoulders and thighs, despite so many medical interventions and healthy lifestyle adjustments.

The chiropractor was at four, as in four-years old, when her questions of abuse would interrupt. I had very few memories before that age at all, and what I had held onto were good ones.

"No!" I answered back quickly, loudly, without thinking.

I was frazzled today when I came in. I thought I hid it well under my make-up and a smile. News of someone close to me seeking treatment for alcohol addiction was still top of mind. I held onto that too, identifying with it, taking it in, as though this news had anything to do with me. I did not know yet, how to use my empathy to feel gratitude and joy for the person whose heart I felt so deeply connected to. I didn't know how to breathe in this wonderful news like a celebration of life and breathe it right back out with joy and best wishes—to find thanks and relief for someone who white-knuckled life for so long and had finally allowed themselves to ask for the help they needed. I couldn't do that yet. I took it in, took it on, and let it be one more thing to worry about, hold on to, and weigh me down. This was another secret to keep. I would turn it to darkness and lock it away, I unconsciously thought, rather than see it as a lesson to ask for help myself.

But then this unexpected treatment as I sat on the table in the yellow room at the chiropractor's office wouldn't allow me to do that. Was it a treatment? I didn't know, but I didn't like losing control like that.

"I don't remember anything traumatic from when I was that young. I don't remember much at all, really. Definitely not from any age younger than that. The trouble I remember was from when I was older, like preteen and teen years."

"That's OK. You don't have to remember it for it to have happened," she answered.

"It wasn't that bad," I continued trying to convince her.

"It doesn't matter," she answered flatly. "It doesn't matter how *bad* you think it is or was. It happened. Your body remembers it. That's all."

I wrapped my arms around myself then, like I was giving myself a hug, at my doctor's prompting. Then I bowed my head and cried some more, as the pseudo psychologist tapped the space between my shoulder blades gently. When there were no more tears, the visit would end in a hug. I left the parking lot alone and confused and tired. I didn't know why I was so emotional about things I didn't understand or maybe even remember from my childhood being brought up, but I was no longer able to ignore it or forget it away again.

Something inside me broke open that day, cut a deep fissure right to the very center of my being. Things began spilling out that I had hidden for so long, much of it I thought I'd forgotten completely. The illusion of ignoring the pain or covering it up began to shatter. The leakage didn't burst out in one quick release of all I had been suppressing. Instead, it seeped slowly like a thick black sludge. It covered me, sticking to me in the form of anger and regret and self-loathing and victimhood.

I found mirrors of the darkness rising from within in the lyrics of songs like "I'm Alive" by Sia. The way it spoke of surviving the storms of life **alone** felt so familiar but only fanned the flames of my newfound anger. I played the song, full volume, as I cooked dinner and screamed the lyrics through unrestrained tears on desolate dirt roads while I ran, as though I was finally yelling them to the parents I'd never before allowed myself to feel negative emotions toward. Each time, remembering as if for the first time, the ways I learned to play, grow, and survive—alone.

This type of anger was a new to me. I had kept such a tight lock on my emotions in all my efforts at forgetting and perfecting. Anger would occasionally, unconsciously, burst forth in a loss of patience or after too long a time of bottling it up so tightly, like that first twist of a cap on a carbonated beverage. It would never burst unexpectedly at someone I was harboring anger for. No. When anger surprised me in the past, it was always directed at my daughters, the most defenseless and undeserving, in the privacy of our home when no one else was around. I yelled at them sometimes when I lost my patience. That always ended in apologies and more pilings of guilt and shame that I covered over and numbed away with more superficial perfecting.

This was not that kind of anger, though. This new feeling hung on me like wet clothes, heavy and uncomfortable. Each time I thought I shook it loose or got rid of it, there it was again. It felt as though darkness itself was clinging to me like thick, black tar.

I tried to forget that song. I removed it from my playlist.

Still, the anger rose. I tried to deny it and cover it up as I thought I'd done successfully for so long, but this hole in my soul would not be silenced that way any longer.

I found a new song, "I'm On Fire" by Bruce Springstein, mostly just the one verse in it describing perfectly how I felt about what had happened to my soul—like someone dug so deep inside me, cutting a chasm right to my core.

This one didn't help either. I tried to put it aside too, but the anger just kept coming. It rose and bubbled and spewed over until, finally, I raged. I quit trying to stop it then. I remembered the first song again, listened to them both now. I raged and raged, when I thought no one else could hear or see. I cried out with all the pain I'd kept tightly controlled for all the years before.

It wasn't until I found myself in a room bursting with light, yet I was covered in a thick sludge of darkness—that I realized my old tricks weren't going to work any longer. I couldn't keep them up. I knew in my heart that I wouldn't be able to numb, pretend, or distract myself from what I was hiding any longer. I knew that the self-hatred, lack of purpose, the loss of direction, and utterly unrecognizable form I found myself in would only grow. There was a small and quiet voice from within that was whispering to me about stopping my life here. It was gaining strength and beginning to persuade me that there might be no reason to go on—that voice would only get louder and stronger if I continued to attempt to hide my darkness, my pain. I was so afraid of finally facing all that I had been hiding, but I was even more afraid of what that voice showed me I was capable of if I didn't.

—

Invitation:

Are there any emotions you've been suppressing because you fear the expression of those emotions or the reactions of others when you do express them? *When the Body Says No* by Gabor Mate, M.D. explores the connection between suppressed emotions and chronic illness and autoimmune disease. There is significant research, as well as case study evidence, to support the mind-body connection in this way. What emotions or feelings are you afraid of or choosing not to share with others? What might happen if you chose to allow yourself to feel and release them? Begin noticing what circumstances or experiences trigger these feelings and what your typical response to those triggers are. Now, instead of pushing them down, denying, or ignoring them, tune into your body, noticing what these emotions feel like in your body. Where do you feel it? What does it feel like? Try letting it pass naturally, taking as long as it needs. Consider sharing what you're feeling with someone in your life (maybe a medical health professional) that you can trust. Could you make a date to have a *real* conversation with them about even a small part of what you're feeling and going through? What would that sound like? Write about and plan for all of the above in your journal.

Real: Bottom

"While the light saved me from drowning, it was the dark that taught me how to swim." - Thais Sky

Did all of my bottoms happen on the couch? Is that where I allowed myself to wallow, to get so low, that the only next step was swift, committed action or death. Not a quick death either but a slow and painful one, most likely grasping at the ankles of those closest to me, pulling them down, down, down into the muck with me.

I remember a couch moment in the not so distant past (a couple of years before leaving teaching) as well, one where I had this choice presented to me—either get up off the couch and choose to make something of this one and only life you've been gifted (the one with two beautiful, joyful children and a husband supporting you) or die a slow and aching death. Sounds from my family playing together in the backyard as I lay exhausted and aching under my down comforter on the brown, leather couch in the living room were hard to ignore. This was typical weekend posture for me, and for so many who suffer with chronic illness I gather, after spending the week working, shuttling, cooking, cleaning, and surviving. Being in the living room gave me a false sense of living with my family. Better than stuck in bed away from them all day, I thought. But that moment, hearing their joy outside in the sun, living an active life helped me realize I wasn't really living, not on the couch under a blanket. I chose life that day and in the days to follow, when I got up off the couch to join them. It was rarely easy or simple, that choice for life. It had required setting a clear intention of truly living, of soaking up the love and joy that was my little family, of doing (even when I was bone-deep tired or I hurt or I didn't feel well) rather than watching others go on living around me.

Somehow, all of those intentional steps led me to another moment, on a different couch, but a couch just the same. I was on my side, in the full-on drama of the fetal position, just lying there on that red, flowered, overstuffed couch in the sunroom of my home. Everything was flooded with light outside me, but the inside was full of more darkness than I'd ever seen before.

This darkness came only after making so many steps to take care of my health. I had left my job, a job where I found joy and success but where I also found stress and the fatigue of mounting responsibilities. I learned to prioritize feeding my body with nutrient-dense foods. I seemingly had everything I'd ever wanted, this stay-at-home-mom life, where I should have found joy in having the time and energy to be the best wife and mom I could be. I should have known from the past that appearances can, in fact, be deceiving. The grass is not always greener.

Yet, I found myself here on the couch. Again. Now, I have never thought I wanted to kill myself, exactly. I've never thought those words in that particular order, but that brilliant, sun-soaked day brought me as close to that thought as I hope to ever come. On that day, as I lay alone, avoiding connection—my family left for the day to go play on the family ranch without me at my insistence—I didn't think about killing myself. I just thought a lot about wanting to die.

I thought about how insignificant I felt. I thought about how, without realizing it, I'd designed my whole life around taking care of my two daughters and my husband. Then I thought about how they really didn't need me at all. They knew how to feed themselves and clean the house if they ever decided they cared about that anyway. That led to me thinking about how pathetic I was for allowing myself to be so insignificant that I could be erased without a care. And then I did it. I let myself go there.

"It truly wouldn't matter if I died," I thought.

This idea of being so insignificant that my death would be of very little consequence, allowed me to settle on the most depressing thought of all.

"If the people I have designed my life around really don't need me, why am I trying to stick around at all? I think…yeah, it would be okay if I died. Maybe, it would be *better*…far fewer medical bills."

The scariest thing I've come to learn about this darkness of the soul is that it's so very unrecognizable when you're in it. The depths of depression blurred my vision so much that I no longer knew where I was at all. With no familiar landmarks, there's no memory of going in, no way of knowing how to get out. I wouldn't actually become conscious of it until at least a bit of that darkness had lifted. This meant that for months, most likely, I walked around and carried on with my daily chores and duties in some sort of zombie-like state. Just going through the motions of day-to-day life in the detached way of someone who wants to die. I have to imagine, because those months, if not lost to me altogether, are a distinctive blur. It wasn't until the following spring that I began to awake from this trance. In doing so, these thoughts and that moment began to come back to me, and I started to understand just how deep I'd been.

I was depressed, but I was waking up a bit at a time. The fog was beginning to lift. Here's the thing about waking up, in the figurative way, of course: once you wake up you can't go back to sleep. At least, it's really, really hard to do. What's the saying? Once you see it, you can't unsee. This was the hope about my deepest depression—I never wanted to go back there again. I did know at that moment, as the tingling sensations of life started to fill my limbs once more, that I would do anything in my power to figure out how I got there and take steps to assure I didn't get lost down that road again.

Some things truly are clearer in the rear view mirror, and this pit of a stop in the road-trip of my life was one of those. Let's pause to take a little review, check out how I ended up here in the first place.

A (not so) brief outline:

1. Girl experiences un-nameable trauma in the super simple and emotionally uncomplex preteen and teenage years of her life (sarcasm dripping).

2. Girl carries on as though this trauma never happened. She is the positive Pollyanna of any group, finding it so easy to forgive and put a nice spin on things when she never acknowledges the hurt in the first place.

3. Girl tries things like alcohol and sex and even some drugs to numb away the pain and loneliness that comes with shoving hurts and traumas down deep in her soul where no one can ever find them, including herself.

4. Girl realizes boys and booze and drugs don't work. They actually add to the shame and pain that she's hidden away. She's gotten really good at that now.

5. Girl learns to blend and hide, just like she hides her pain. She fades well into the background, doing everything she can to *not* stand out.

6. Girl begins to build her identity around being everything to everyone. She knows what others need and she is great at working hard to make it happen. She is here to serve, forgetting always to serve herself. She will be the perfect wife. She will be the perfect mom. She will be the perfect teacher. People really like this girl, almost everyone. She will please as many of them as she can.

7. Girl likes it when people like her. It makes her feel good about herself. It makes her forget all the things she's been trying to forget until they almost don't exist at all.

8. Girl gets better and better at making other people feel good.

9. Girl loses herself in the process. She looks and acts like a woman on the outside, but she can't shake the feeling of being a child on the inside.

10. Girl's body cries out in pain. She ignores that until parts of the girl's body literally explode inside her. She has lost herself so completely that she doesn't even trust herself or her pain enough to plead for help until this happens.

11. Girl thinks this is a lesson on how she can serve others in her life (daughter, husband, other loved ones) better in the future so that *they* don't experience the same medical issues.

12. Girl, now with more scars, continues her perfecting, pleasing, serving, covering up, hiding, stuffing, ignoring. She's getting even better at it. She has so much practice now.

13. Girl's body begins to experience so much pain that she can no longer serve others in her life the way she done before. Her body is so loud about this, that she can no longer hide it. Her joints are hot and red. She limps a bit when she walks. She can't mow the lawn (to please her husband and her neighbors and lots of other people who aren't watching and don't even care) without making her wrists and elbows and shoulders hurt so much that she finds it impossible to push a shopping cart the next day. She does it anyway.

14. Girl goes to the doctor.

15. Girl gets more doctors. They tell her she's sick, really sick. They don't say really sick, but they say things like, "rare" and look at her in a way that's all mixed up with pity and fascination and interest. Doctors like rare things they can pity. The girl thinks maybe she's relieved to be fascinatingly sick. Maybe she has permission to take a break from pleasing everyone else now.

16. Girl takes a bunch of pills. Every day. Several times a day. She eats *only* chocolate bars. She drinks only Diet Pepsi. She gets thinner. She is pretty on the outside. People notice this. They tell her how good she looks. This makes her feel good, even more perfect.

17. Girl begins to see little glimmers of an idea that perfect on the outside does not mean perfect on the inside. She feels her dirtiness, her loneliness, the dirt she's been hiding since she was a little girl. She feels it now. She can't hide it from herself anymore. But others, they still don't know. They don't see it. The thinner she gets, the more they like her, she thinks. They tell her how pretty she is, how thin she is, how they want to be more like her.

18. Girl gets more doctors and many, many more tests. She gets a lot of those looks, the ones that make a doctor's face say things without actually saying them.

19. Girl's doctor says, "It's too bad you have to work."

20. Girl asks herself, "Do I have to work?"

21. Girl quits. She cries a lot. She's consumed by guilt and uncertainty and worry, but she quits anyway. She decides she can take time to heal—the pain in her joints and her muscles, superficial stuff like that.

22. Girl quickly makes this about serving others again. She volunteers on boards. She joins multi-level marketing companies to earn money from home and prove her worth. She makes breakfasts, packs lunches, and makes perfect dinner dishes. She cleans and washes. She makes it all about everyone else. Again.

23. Girl reads books about healing her physical body. She also reads books like the one about shame by Brené Brown and *Miracle Morning* by Hal Elrod.

24. Girl steps into the office of a "chiropractor." She gets probiotics. She gets her chakras aligned. AND a box is opened up inside her that she can't put a lid on. She can't close the door, or cover it up, or hide it, or make it go away by asking other people what they need.

25. Girl finds herself on the couch, in the sun-room full of light. She's full of darkness and dirt and self-hatred. She doesn't know how to shake it, because she's only just remembered it existed. She forgot about all these things when she got so good at hiding them, at covering them up with perfect. She can't forget them now. She feels insignificant. She feels worthless. She wants to die.

—

Still, there was another voice calling from within too, the one that remembered the beautifully wild soul I carried with me from childhood; the one that loved that little girl of my past as much as I loved the two girls I had brought into the world. My daughters deserved a mother that could foster that wildness within their still pure souls. They deserved a guide that could help them manifest all of the unique goodness within them. *They* deserved it, even if I couldn't find that worthiness within myself.

It was that thought and that voice within me that hadn't given up yet, that gave me the smallest bits of strength to do what was necessary. That voice reminded me that if I didn't do the real work of stripping myself naked, down to the pain I covered with so many things through the years—boys, booze, isolation, people-pleasing, perfectionism—the quiet whispers to give up would only grow into a convincing voice to end my life. That voice that told me the world was no different, no better, with me in it, there was only one way to quiet it.

It wouldn't be easy. I knew that. I spent a lifetime covering it with so many distractions to avoid it. This time, I had to sit with that darkness—the shame, the fear, the unworthiness, the anger, the self-loathing—I would sit there covered in it. I would acknowledge its existence within me, finally. I would call it by name. I would sift through it, taking each grimy, sticky bit from within, pulling them out and laying them before me to examine. I would cleanse my soul of it, not by hiding or denying or minimizing or shallowly-forgiving it away. No. Not this time. This time I'd stand up straight, stripped naked, and I would walk right through it all. Only then would I, could I, find my way out.

—

Invitation:

If you are experiencing depression, suicidal thoughts, or suicidal ideation, please seek help from a loved one or mental health professional. You can find help and support by calling the National Suicide Prevention Lifeline: 800-273-8255.

Can you remember the major points in your life that got you from point A to point NOW? Make a timeline of your life with the most pivotal moments in your memory. What can you celebrate? What is at least one thing you can look back on and thank yourself for doing? Thank yourself for being such a badass. What is one pattern or choice you would benefit from changing in the future? Make a plan to move forward without that tired trait. Journal your ideas.

Real: It Could Be Worse

"As long as you keep secrets and suppress information, you are fundamentally at war with yourself…The critical issue is allowing yourself to know what you know. That takes an enormous amount of courage." - Bessel A. van der Kolk, The Body Keeps the Score

There's a phrase that's crossed my mind far too many times to keep an accurate record through the years. I've heard it echoed in vulnerable conversations with others about events they've endured and survived. *It could be worse* became a phrase I repeated so often to myself, it might as well have been my mantra. That phrase got me through most of the difficult moments in my life; two drunk step-dads, feeling poor in all the ways, unconscious feelings of abandonment, settling for good enough, chronic illnesses and confusing diagnoses—all the really tough moments. It helped me figure out how to grin and bear it, find what I could to be grateful for, push on, work hard, and work through difficult circumstances.

Not long after gaining the first inklings of the autoimmune diseases deteriorating my body, I found a lump in my right breast. I was reclined in a chair, relaxing and watching a movie, and for reasons that escape me now, I must have decided to do one of the checks women are so frequently reminded are important. There was no way to know if it was the position I was in that made the lump so easily palpable or if it was that it was new and quickly growing. I couldn't answer that question, because I rarely checked for lumps at all. I kept the discovery to myself for several days, until one night in bed I decided to tell my husband.

"I think you *have* to," his response to my question of whether or not I should get it checked out.

That's how I found myself getting a mammogram just before my thirty-fourth birthday. Something about the nature of the lump in the mammogram pictures led to a biopsy. The polyp found in the biopsy led to a precautionary surgery to remove the entire lump, so that it could be entirely dissected for signs of cancer. For several months I silently worried that I could have breast cancer in addition to autoimmune diseases. Only four people knew what I was going through, including the nurse practitioner that ordered the mammogram, the same one that had ordered the labs pointing to lupus not long before. My husband and two friends from work knew too, one who supportively accompanied me to an appointment with the surgeon, and another I had to tell because I had to decline one of our regular runs together after my surgery.

When the results came back that the lump was benign, I had another reason to tell myself, *it could be worse*, just as I'd done so many times before. I was so incredibly and sincerely grateful to not be diagnosed with breast cancer, that any complaining about what I did have felt blasphemous. It most certainly could have been much worse. I knew that, once again. So, I moved on, without ever truly moving through what I was experiencing rather than what I *wasn't*.

I've heard other iterations of the same phrase, as well, in my own mind and from the lips of many. *It's not that bad. It wasn't that bad*—frequently repeated phrases that worked just like the first. The final sentiment has been passed to me in conversations with my mom about our shared history and from so many other "tough" individuals describing their own struggles. All these phrases were helpful to me for a time. They were a coping mechanism that lead me to an outwardly healthy life. They worked, for a while, until they didn't.

It's true, things *could be worse.* It could have been worse. It could always be worse. Others have had it much worse than I have. Truth! There are darknesses that exist in our world that I've never experienced. I acknowledge them and empathize deeply with their survivors, because I have not felt them exactly, but I've had my own taste of darkness. My own taste of darkness is what has allowed me to hold such deep empathy for so many. This empathy is arguably the greatest gift my darkness has given me. The problem is, this phrase is only helpful to a point. After that, it just perpetuates an unhealthy cycle, the one that allowed me to deny and ignore what was causing my emotional distress rather than deal with it, eventually leading to physical and mental illness. It also brings blame and shame to the victim for speaking up.

Let's just get it out of the way now. It could be worse. It could have been worse. It may be worse in the future. I know that. You know that. Now that it's been clearly stated, it doesn't matter anymore. To move on, to heal, to improve my physical and emotional health, I had to throw that phrase out the window. Moving forward meant finally dealing with the past. The past was only one thing—what it was—not better or worse, just what it was.

Moving on…

—

Invitation:

Have you ever told yourself, "It could be worse."? Have you ever minimized or denied your pain, because you felt acknowledging it meant you were ungrateful for all of the good or that you would be labeled a complainer? Are you willing to be open to the idea that this doesn't help you or anyone who may actually have it "worse" than you? What if by acknowledging your trials, trauma, and/or pain you're able to heal from them? What if by healing from that pain you're able to share it with others, allowing them to heal as well? Would you be willing to share then? Would you worry as much about if it could be worse or not? Journal your responses to these questions.

Real: Awakening

"To shed conditioning one layer at a time takes courage, as you must trust in a self you do not yet fully recognize." - Alana Fairchild

There are phrases that I couldn't say (sometimes still can't), or even think, without bringing tears to my eyes. Phrases like,

"Help me. Help me. Help *ME*!"

or

"You are beautiful (to self). I love you!"

and, going back to that moment in the chiropractor's office,

"I would rather die than stand up for myself."

I was, killing myself literally from the inside out, attacking my own body, silently, before I'd consider asking for help or standing up for myself or even imagining that I could love myself as much as I loved *anyone* else.

The fact that I could exist in the world while being so blind to myself, and my inner dialog, was shocking. No, not just exist, I was a high-functioning human being. I had lived for many, many years. All of that was true, and I could still have ideas and beliefs about myself that were so ingrained in my being that I didn't even realize they were a part of me. Unconscious.

Well, I was awakened. I woke up when that chiropractor cracked open my soul. I stayed awake when the superficial repairs I was used to making wouldn't cover that crack. And remain awake now, as I continue to take the steps toward self-love. I couldn't give myself another job or find a way to earn a bit of money or volunteer for some board or cook an amazing meal or clean my house or pull enough weeds or try to perfect others around me enough to make that crack go away. I tried. I had to do the work of figuring out why those things wouldn't work anymore. That meant cracking open even more. Breaking it apart completely.

It was brutal. It was gut-wrenching. There was nothing pretty or graceful or easy about it. Undoing what I'd spent a lifetime doing wasn't meant to be any of those things.

—

Invitation:

What wound might you still be carrying? Would opening that wound allow some light to enter? What is the outermost layer you could begin to remove in effort to get to the authentic beauty at your core? Write about your ideas.

Real: Saying Goodbye

"No one warns you about the amount of mourning in growth." - Te V. Smith

I died to myself today. I said goodbye to that scared, little girl that added layer upon layer to hide herself from the world, from herself. I attempted it before. This time I meant it.

I shed a tear for her—the version of myself that got me this far. She was good. She served me well for so long. Other people liked her too. She was kind, caring, considerate, empathetic, thoughtful, giving—so many things that I hope to continue to be or find a way to be again, someday. She was also deeply insecure, so deeply that she couldn't even recognize it in herself. She was so afraid of disappointing others, that she'd never even considered what she might be doing to disappoint herself. She was so concerned with the approval of others, that she lost herself completely. She was so scared to trust another with her truest, deepest self, that she couldn't even find those pieces within her any longer.

All of this I am grateful for. It was my method of survival—got me through extended trauma and to this point right here and now. I realized as we rounded a sharp switchback that would take us down into the valley between massive fourteen thousand foot mountain peaks, that where I was right now was an amazing place. My heart was full of gratitude for the life I found myself living.

Riding in the passenger seat of our white, Toyota SUV with the ski rack on top, on the flat two-lane highway surrounded by mountains, I could see all that the scared girl had given to me. Silent tears of grief ran down my cheeks as I stared at the mountains to my right from the valley floor, the contrast of the jagged, white tops to the blue green slopes rising below so evident this time of year. The two girls—my own daughters—in the backseat, now thirteen and eight, had no idea I was mourning, nor did my husband, behind the wheel to my left. They were all absorbed in a podcast and their own thoughts as we left the place that brought us all so much joy, my husband's family cabin in the mountains of Colorado where we'd spent many weekends, including this one, together.

I knew so many of these things were the gifts of my former self—the one I was letting go of now. I could thank that girl for the deep love and connection I felt for my daughters, the ones I would do anything for. I could thank her for the patience and foresight that allowed my marriage to endure and strengthen as the years passed by. I could thank her for the hard work and determination to put temporary aches and desires aside, as I pushed through to help create the life of freedom we all enjoyed today.

These were no small feats. I would be forever grateful for them, but getting to the next place in my life would require shedding that old self, leaving her behind, to become the woman that could keep moving forward. I had to become real. I had to become the authentic woman who knew my own soul's wants and desires and worked courageously to fulfill those. I needed to learn to love and value myself enough to serve myself too—my deepest act of love yet. I would hide and cover no more. I would grow into full acceptance of myself, dirt and all, no more hiding, baring my wild, naked self for all to see.

I didn't have the practice or the strength within me to do it for myself yet. My transformation was for my daughters now—a greater purpose in the lives I'd helped create that were now dosing in the backseat. To fulfill my hope of raising confident and independent women, women who knew themselves well enough to create the lives their souls called for, then I'd have to be that myself first. I knew the only way to teach them was to lead them, to show them by my actions not my words. They would not learn these qualities if I did not also embody them. I'd have to become, at least in part, what I hoped they could find in themselves.

I didn't know what my people-pleasing, insecurity, and perfectionism taught my daughters, but I wished to perpetuate none of the cycles I was now conscious of in my life. So, it was out of love that I said a grateful goodbye to that scared girl within me as the four of us quietly made our way down the road together. I'd lovingly wipe the tear from my cheek, knowing I meant it this time. It would be messy for sure, learning how to move into this new self while transforming the worthy pieces into something that could fill me with life rather than deplete it. It would take grace and time, but I would get there, I knew. I would become, become real.

—

Invitation:

Are there former versions of yourself or old habits and relationship patterns you thought you'd let go of but keep reappearing? What personality traits are you ready to say goodbye to? Is there anything about those versions of yourself or your old patterns that you can be grateful for? What is it about them that no longer serves your vision for yourself and your life? What are you finally ready to bury once and for all? Say it aloud. Say "Thank you for ___________. Now, goodbye. Though I appreciate where you've brought me, I no longer need you." Write it down. Write a farewell letter to your former self, if you'd like. Then, burn that shit, once and for all.

Real: Peeling

"The soul is covered in a thousand veils." - Hazurat Inayat Khan
Remove the veils so that I might see the truth.

Quick fixes don't exist. They never have for me, at least. I've found healing and recovery to be a lot more like peeling the layers of an onion, one at a time. As with onions, it can mean tears are shed and it gets a little stinky, too. But the real truth is, I never found a lightning bolt of a cure or won the lottery when it came to fixing my pain and discomfort. There wasn't just one simple step to getting my body to agree to stop attacking itself. It's been a lot more like goal setting. When we set goals, we don't reach the goal and say, "That's it! I'm done. I reached my goal, and now I can put it all on autopilot for the rest of my days." No. When we reach a goal, we feel good, hopefully, better than before we reached the goal, if it was worth reaching for. Then we set a new goal. We continue reaching. We continue growing. We continue finding ways to improve upon ourselves, our lives, our situations.

It's been like that with my physical and mental health too. There's no arriving. There's no hack for physical and emotional healing. Only after I stopped trying to hack my life, was I able to truly start living it.

Don't get me wrong. I've often sought a quick fix, but what I found was yet another layer to peel back below the one I'd just done some work on. Typically, at first at least, I tried the most obvious "fix" (the 'so obvious it was staring me in the eye, breathing down my neck, stepping on my toes' type of obvious). This meant that when I was literally, without exaggeration, subsisting on Hershey bars and Diet Pepsi, I changed the food I was putting in my body. I fixed my diet. Don't get the wrong impression here, either. It wasn't as though one day I woke up and said to myself, "I'm really doing a number on my body with what I'm choosing to eat. I think I'll change that today. Problem solved! Yeah for me!"

It was more like all the signs were pointing to one issue—the one step I could take in the right direction that would help with almost everything else. There were most likely arrows and neon signs pointing directly at it, but my lists of excuses and cloud of resistance made it really, really hard to see even them. It wasn't until my husband sat me down, clearly defined the problem, and directly outlined the chosen solution, that I even considered taking this first step. Even then, it wasn't pretty. I didn't put a smile on my face, roll up my sleeves, and get to work, whistling as I did so. It was more like going through the various stages of grief—denial, anger, bargaining, depression, and acceptance. Except I circled back to anger a lot, particularly anger at my husband. I found it pretty easy to blame him in this case.

It went something like:

Husband: Debbie, I think it's time to do something about our diet.

Denial Debbie: What? (look of complete shock on my face as I'm putting the third snack-sized Hershey bar in my mouth for dinner while laying on the couch watching television)

Husband: Well, I don't think the way I'm eating is doing me any good, and I'm pretty sure (his finger pointing at the direct evidence) the way you're eating isn't doing you any good either.

Denial Debbie: Well, (pausing to wash the last bit of chocolate down with a gulp of Diet Pepsi) I'm barely eating anything lately because I feel so sick from medication. Eating a few vegetables isn't going to make everything better.

Husband: Well, it wouldn't *hurt*, right?

Mad Debbie: That's easy for you to say. You don't feel nauseous all the time.

Husband: Do you think chocolate and diet soda will make you less nauseous?

Mad Debbie: I didn't say that, but it's the only thing that even sounds stomachable. If you take that away, I won't be able to eat anything.

Husband: I'm not taking anything away. I'm just saying there's clearly a problem. It's worth a try to see if changing what you're eating will help you feel better.

Mad Debbie: The rheumatologist said food won't change anything. You think you know more than my rheumatologist?

Husband: Have you seen your rheumatologist?

This was a slight at my doctor, but it's true that he didn't look like he felt any better than I did at that moment. His body showed pretty clear signs of maltreatment.

Bargaining Debbie: Fine! I see your point, but I'm not doing Weight Watchers again. I'm not counting points or stepping on a scale every day. My weight is well within normal according to the BMI, and I don't think it's that healthy of a system anyway.

Husband: I never said I wanted to do Weight Watchers again.

Bargaining Debbie: What do you want to do then? I don't know if the same thing makes sense for both of us.

Husband: I think it will be easier for us both if we do the same thing. I"ve been reading about a diet that goes in phases. In the first phase you cut out all sugar and grains for at least two...

Mad, Interrupting Debbie: What!?! (my arguing cut short by coughing and choking on a chocolate bar).

Husband: It's just for two weeks, and there are these message boards where people help support each other. I'll show you, if you want. They share recipes and everything.

Denial Debbie: No sugar or any grains? I don't even know what I'd eat. I don't have the time to cook all of my food. We have two young daughters and I work full-time, remember?

Husband: If we take some time this weekend to make a clear plan and make a shopping list, I think we can do it. We can start reading the book this week.

Depressed Debbie: Ughhh...(lots of looks of pain and discomfort now).

Husband: It's worth a shot.

Debbie: ....

You get the idea. Basically, I had to be beaten over the head before I realized I had a problem. Then I had to be force-fed the solution. Even then, it certainly wasn't a quick fix. Cutting sugars and grains and dramatically increasing the amounts of vegetables I was eating didn't hurt. I did drop nearly twenty pounds of water weight and stored fat from all that extra sugar. It didn't take all of my cares away though, not even when it came to food.

That first diet, in a roundabout way, led to an Eastern Medicine Doctor, which led to an elimination diet. The elimination diet led to a realization that dairy was causing my eczema. Good-bye dairy (a very depressing moment). This surprising discovery with dairy led to a traditional allergy test, that exposed a wheat allergy. Wait! What now? This woman, who wouldn't have complained about being a vegetarian as long as she had her grilled cheese sandwiches and quesadillas, was allergic to wheat and couldn't eat cheese without breaking out in a painful rash? Throw a big hitch right in the middle of everything I thought I knew, why don't you.

That allergy test led to the discovery of the autoimmune paleo/protocol (AIP) diet which led to something called a delayed allergy test or IgG, where I find myself today—in a world where I don't eat wheat or dairy or eggs or yeast or mushrooms or cranberries or...you get the idea.

See what I mean? It's like an onion. It's one layer at a time. Not a quick fix at all. I'm actually grateful for that now. Could you imagine if one day you ate and drank literally anything you wanted, and the next, you were forced to cut your very favorite foods plus a bunch of weird little ones? That would have been more difficult and most likely set me up for a lot of failure and disappointment. Though that happened, too. It just happened in little bits along the way.

You may find yourself wondering what other fixes I've tried, what other layers I've peeled back. Well, there's quite a list. I'm still going. I've learned to be OK with that, comforted by it, even. Perfect health is a fantasy, but taking small steps toward better health one at a time is an achievable reality for us all.

Here are few more of the layers I've peeled back:

- Trying essential oils after a dear friend would just not quit hounding me about them led to fewer doctor visits for the whole family, fewer prescriptions, and an increased feeling of control with my mental and physical well-being.
- Experimenting with food and essential oils caused an obsession with reading labels, which caused a revamp of beauty, skin care, and cleaning products in our home, to decrease toxicity in the products we regularly used.
- Reading a book about brain health (due to my husband's grandfather's struggles with Alzheimer's) led to an entirely new personal discovery of what my intestines have to do with my health at all. This led to a search for probiotics...which led to working on healing my gut so that I could actually absorb the nutrients in the nutrient-dense food I was now putting into my body, leading to discovering the deficiencies my body truly had so that I could supplement them accordingly.
- Probiotics also led, in a very unintended way, to the realization that it's all connected—the physical body, the spiritual body, the emotional body, the energetic body. This *Ah-Ha*! opened up and still continues to bring about layer after layer of healing of not just my physical body, but the others as well, and it's why I'm writing these words.

Layer after layer. There are so many layers. It's not simple or easy or quick, but it's real. Really real. It's also comforting to know that I don't have to tackle it all at once. I just tackle the beast that's most obvious, the one that is staring me right in the face, breathing its sour, foul-smelling breath right where I don't want it. The one that's making me the sickest, right now at this very moment. The one I simply can't ignore any longer.

—

Invitation:

What habits or routines might you be holding onto that are not promoting your mental/physical/emotional health? Is there anything you might be able to control in your daily life, that requires no doctor appointment, prescription, or authority of a professional? What's your hunch about one thing you could change tomorrow that might lead to healing and growth? Journal about this.

Real: Into The Sun

"If the lie of shame (I am something wrong.) exists at the core, everything else becomes cover-up—religion, power, performance." - Unknown

After hearing doctors bring it up for so long, I finally began examining the stress in my life. This, at last, gave me the courage and self-awareness to tell my husband that I wanted to leave my work, to quit teaching and stay home with our youngest daughter, who was four years old and about to enter preschool. This was in part out of a genuine sincerity—I needed to slow down and I was feeling burn-out after years of service. I found it increasingly difficult to keep up with the healthy diet and exercise I felt integral to control the progression of my autoimmune conditions. It was also another way to feed my addiction to perfectionism. The unconscious thinking at that time being that, if I could stay home from work, I could turn the dial up uncountable notches on being the best mom and wife my thirty-something self could be. I would have time and energy to cook the best food, pack the best lunches, maintain a consistently sparkling home, be in the best physical shape, and on and on and on. One more layer peeled back, but leveling up on my need to be perfect the whole time.

The truth of what happened when I left the job (that I had hitched my entire life's purpose to for so many years) was not what was expected. For years I had justified going to work, rather than staying home to mother our daughters, by saying it was God's calling for my life. I had made myself feel likable, gained approval, and found all of my worthiness from a job. Teaching is a difficult and noble profession, but I could have found just as much of "God's calling" in staying home to nurture and grow a family. It wasn't about careers or callings or noble service, it was about the thing, under-the-thing, under-the-thing, for me.

By stripping off the biggest layer I'd wrapped around myself, the one that made me feel worthy, good at something, admirable—the greatest fuel to my addiction to perfectionism—I was left with the truth.

When cooking for my family and cleaning the house didn't make me feel better physically, or make me feel fulfilled or fill me with purpose, I found myself hopeless on the couch. I felt entirely and utterly useless. It became clear to me that my family could cook and clean for themselves. They would not become homeless or starve to death if my life were to end at that very moment. My daughters were old enough and my husband self-sufficient enough that they would keep moving forward with their lives, with or without me. There would be sadness or grief in my absence. I knew that. But they are beautiful, brilliant souls that would continue on in remarkable ways even if I was gone. Good thing!

My dark-night-of-the-soul moment, when I found myself on the couch in my sun room, was one of the greatest gifts I've been given. Peeling away the layers to get to the thing under-the-thing-under-the-thing allowed me to ask myself a question.

If I'm not here to be a perfect mother or a perfect wife or a perfect teacher...(or a perfect cook or a have a perfectly clean house or a perfectly, weed-free lawn or a perfect body or perfect hair or perfect face or anything perfect at all), *then why am I here? Why am I still here?*

That moment was the first time, in my life of thirty-something years, that it occurred to me that my purpose on this planet was not to continually become more and more perfect. Clearly, I wasn't perfect, but I had been trying so very hard to be. Still I was here, on this couch, in despair, feeling useless and tired and like I'd had enough. Only then did it occur to me that maybe the point wasn't to be perfect at all, maybe the point was to be *real*.

The way out of that darkness for me, was the question: *Why?* The only answer I had at the time was *I don't know*. I didn't. I had no idea what I wanted or why I was here, and I didn't have enough love for myself to get up off the couch for *me*.

The beginning of the answer to that question was from a TED talk by Glennon Doyle Melton. In it she talks about addiction and mental illness and the struggles of life that we can all relate to. She doesn't separate drug and alcohol addiction from more societally acceptable things like snark and working too much. She doesn't even separate addiction from perfectionism. I watched her speak and for the first time, it occurred to me that my addiction just might be perfectionism. Her descriptive words compare addictions to capes that we put on to prove ourselves as the superheroes the world wants us to be. The visual image of me putting on my superhero cape of perfectionism reminded me of an old, favorite song, "Closer to Fine" by The Indigo Girls. Had I wrapped my capes of perfectionism and people-pleasing so tightly around myself in fear, like a blanket, warm and safe? Had I done so until the very things I thought were protecting me began to smother the life out of me? Is that what I'd done?

I built my identity around taking what I knew about other people and using it to serve them: in my career, to serve the children and the people that I worked with; in my life at home, to serve my own children, my husband, my extended family.

It felt so good—consuming myself with being exactly what everyone else needed—the perfect way to continue to deny and stuff and cover up all the pain and discomfort of my youth. It did all this while also enabling an overwhelming desire to please others. What could be more pleasing than perfect? A selfless mother, wife, co-worker, team member, daughter, sister, daughter-in-law, granddaughter. I tried to be everything to everyone by covering myself in these capes.

The obvious problem here is that no one knew the real person under that cape. Of course, I wasn't perfect, and I wasn't fooling anyone. Pleasing them, yes. Fooling them, no. Though, I did a pretty good job of fooling myself.

Perfectionism was socially acceptable, much more so than alcohol or drug addiction. Keeping my house, my marriage, my appearance, the appearance of my children just so, everything so very neat and tidy—people really liked that. Working really hard in the service of others—they were okay with that, too.

For many years, perfectionism and people-pleasing served me well. Until they didn't. When I continued to ignore the aches and pains of my heart and soul, my physical body began to ache. My body began to attack itself. I couldn't see the destruction that had been done to the inner fabric of my lungs, but I couldn't ignore the pain in my legs and hips and fingers and wrists and elbows and the very soles of my feet any longer. Those things made it harder to look perfect. Superficial perfection became increasingly hard when I struggled to braid my daughters' hair, blow dry my own rapidly-thinning hair, walked with a limp, and had trouble pushing a shopping cart.

These symptoms screaming in a way that could no longer be ignored, forced me to question my actions and take a long look at myself. They eventually allowed me to walk away from my job and begin the work of taking care of myself.

The day I walked into that chiropractor's office and asked for a bottle of probiotics, the chiropractor saw right through me. That chiropractor didn't see the cape of perfection I spent a decade and a half building. She saw the things within my soul that I could no longer mask in a cape. That cape was a fraud, and my chiropractor knew it, even if I didn't. She opened up a crack in me, a crack that began to expose the inner workings of a woman so good at hiding for so long. When I didn't have a job to tie to a greater purpose, to spackle over each crack and cover them up again, I didn't know what to do anymore. I couldn't slap some paint on it and move on with a smile. I couldn't hide it any longer, not even from myself.

When I began to ask myself questions like,

What's wrong with you?

Why aren't you happy?

What do you want?

I had no answers. I had a great life. It looked so perfect on the outside, but in the depths of my soul, was a darkness I had never let out. I thought I wanted to quit my job. I thought that would solve all of my problems, and when it didn't, I found that I didn't even know what I wanted without asking someone else what they wanted first. That realization only added to the heavy pit of shame I had yet to consciously discover.

What I began to find when I looked within, was a self-loathing of such magnitude I had to quickly look away again. When I tried to ask myself what I wanted, what I might need, all I found were answers about how pathetic a thirty-something woman must be to have gotten this far in life without even knowing herself at all.

What a sad, pathetic woman you are. You didn't even know just how much you hate yourself. I slung the worst insults at myself, and for the first time, I could really hear them.

As I sat there listening to Glennon's words I began asking more questions. I was led to the answers, one-by-one, little-by-little. They came in the form of chats with a neighbor that led me to a chiropractor. They came in phone calls with a friend, who'd saved me more than once, when we decided to start a blog together. The answers required the smallest of steps, like reading the book Miracle Morning by Hal Elrod that I heard mentioned in a podcast. Answers came in watching another TED talk on shame by Brené Brown and reading her books. The answers were not huge leaps or giant steps, though some of them did feel like it at the time.

The answers were just taking the very next step, the small one right in front of me. Trusting the whispers coming from my soul a tiny bit at a time. That and the thought of serving a true purpose to my daughters, beyond cooking and washing their clothes, though those things are worthy too. My purpose for my girls at that point was getting off the couch and becoming the kind of woman that could break the cycle of fear and helplessness and playing small. I would become a woman who knew what she wanted and went after it, with passion and determination. A woman who took leaps and over-reached and failed and then got right back up again and kept going for it.

I had no idea how. Yet. I didn't even know what I wanted or who I was or why I was here, but I was finally ready to do the real work of figuring that out.

I kept peeling back, going for the next thing-under-the-thing. I kept clawing my way from the darkness of my soul. As I did so, learning to meditate, to journal, practice yoga, reading, etc., Glennon Doyle's words continued to ring out in my mind:

> "The sun shows up every morning, no matter how bad you've been the night before. It shines without judgment. It never withholds. It warms the sinners, the saints, the druggies, the cheerleaders—the saved and the heathens alike. You can hide from the sun, but it won't take you personally. It'll never, ever punish you for hiding. You can stay in the dark for years or decades, and when you finally step outside, it'll be there."

Feeling sad and pathetic and full of hate may not seem like a good place to start, but it was the very place my most difficult transformation began. I couldn't hide anymore. I couldn't deny or forget what had brought me to this place. I couldn't cover it up with make-up and a smile or by eating better or exercising more or quitting my job. I had done all those things already. The next step could only be taken by doing the work I'd been putting off for so long. It was time for the real work to begin. It was time for the rising.

—

Invitation:

In her TED talk, *Lessons from the Mental Hospital*, Glennon Melton says, "But we all have our own capes, don't we? Perfectionism, overworking, snarkiness, apathy…they're all superhero capes. And our capes are what we put over our real selves so that our real, tender selves don't have to be seen and can't be hurt." For a moment, consider the possibility that you may be protecting yourself with a cape. Maybe your cape is obvious, like drugs or alcohol. Or maybe it's much harder to identify, like buying things, or eating things, or achieving things. Can you think of something you've used in your life to cover-up and protect yourself from the world or numb yourself from the pain and discomfort you feel when you show up in it? Maybe the answer is perfectly clear or maybe it's just a glimmer of an idea you're just barely beginning to see. Write all about it, either way. What behavior(s) might be your possible cape(s)? How does it make you feel when you put it on? What might it feel like to take it off?

Next, get quiet. Remove any distractions and focus on your breath—three, deep breaths, in and out, slowly. Now, listen. Do you hear your intuition speaking to you? Do you hear your soul calling? It won't sound like a list or nagging or bullying or anger or fear or resentment. It may sound like curiosity. It may sound like a hunch. It may sound like an idea or a question you've had that just won't go away no matter how long you've tried to ignore it. What is your intuition telling you? What is it asking you to do? What is one step you can take today (or tomorrow) in faith and trust? Write all about that too.

Real: Adult Children of Alcoholics

"Are you willing to transform? To give up; be the fool; re-write your story; not recognize yourself; believe differently; be something, someone you have not yet known?... You can start a revolution with a lightning bolt or by burning one limiting belief at a time." - *Danielle LaPorte*

There was a moment of clarity after I'd allowed stillness to seep in, after I'd stripped away all the distractions of a typically busy life of a modern, middle-class mother and wife and teacher in the United States. There was no job to go to every morning to perfect and people-please my way through. My kids were now being schooled at home, and I had cleared their schedule enough to allow for routine breathers throughout the days and weeks. There were things to be done, but after that, I was just left with myself and my thoughts, a place where I ought to find peace and clarity after eliminating the busyness I thought was creating the stress in my life. To my surprise, I did not find peace or clarity there. It did not escape me either, that I was a middle-class, white woman with a life and lifestyle that should have led me to a place of gratitude, by societal standards, not darkness.

The clear moment came as I was scrolling through a social media feed, slowing to read a post. The exact words and phrasing are lost to me now, but the overall sentiment is not. This post was a graphic, listing various ways that adults raised by alcoholics might continue to be affected by their upbringing. I learned that these adults are called Adult Children of Alcoholics, or ACoA as they've affectionately termed themselves.

I had been through years of diagnosing physical symptoms at this point. I had gone to numerous specialists and been a willing subject of test after test trying to figure out what was *wrong* with me. At this time, only one of those specialists had posed the question of managing stress to manage symptoms and creating a sacred (my adjective) routine. Those were the only two hints that my mental health may have an effect on my physical health. I took both as an insult at the time, interpreting them as a way of saying the illnesses causing so much physical, daily pain and exhaustion may all be in my mind. I didn't understand.

It wasn't until that visit to the chiropractor that an opening took place. That visit cracked open a piece of me that I'd been hiding away, and in doing so, also cracked the armor of my ego that was afraid to admit to any connection between my childhood and my present state of helplessness. I had survived for so long with the narratives of:

"Just keep pushing."

"Work harder."

"Hustle more."

"You should be grateful for what you have."

"If you were grateful enough, you wouldn't feel so lost, lonely, and depressed."

"Re-frame it into something positive."

"Other people have it much worse than you."

"It could always be worse."

"You're fine."

"You're OK."

But I wasn't fine, and I clearly wasn't OK. I was spending untold hours in doctors' offices, waiting rooms, at pharmacy counters, and still searching for alternative treatments that could cure me. Things were not OK. I was not fine, yet it never occurred to me that it might be helpful to consider my mental health—that *that* may have some effect physically. That seemed like some crazy, mystical, far-out idea.

Then that day, in the chiropractor's office, a new synapse began to form—just the first threads being woven—this idea that it might be time to examine what actually happened to me in adolescence and that it may have a lasting effect on where I found myself today. That small sliver of an opening allowed me to read this new information about ACoA, take it in, relate to it, and not immediately forget about it and forge on. I began, in that moment, to not only examine why I related to it so deeply but also how it allowed me to dig deeper. What I had been doing to this point wasn't working, after all. Why not begin to think about something new.

So, in a rare moment of openness and trust, what would later become a conscious, difficult, and repeated pattern of deep healing, I took this tiny spark of an idea to my husband that night in bed. I cried as I told him that I read something that I related to. I'm sure I apologized for my tears, but I let myself keep going as I read aloud to him about the adult behaviors of children traumatized by alcoholic adults in their lives. He listened as I told him how they judge themselves without mercy; have difficulty with intimacy and relationships; constantly seek approval and affirmation; feel deeply different from people around them; are extremely loyal even when loyalty is undeserved; are self-loathing; love people who need rescuing; hide their feelings and numb themselves until they eventually have trouble feeling anything at all. I don't remember now the exact words I read to him. I do remember the hiccuping sobs that made it hard to understand the words I was reading. He listened intently anyway, holding my free hand as I cried and read. Then, maybe as an act to further protect my ego and disclose as little as possible, I asked him, "Can you relate to any of those things?"

I laugh now at the glaring conspicuousness of such a question. He answered back, in the kindest way, "I don't know, but it seems like you can. Do you want to talk about it?"

I didn't, but his response and my curiosity gave me just enough hope and just the beginning of trust that would keep me going, keep moving me toward that curiosity, and the tiniest whispers of healing that would come.

—

Invitation:

Consider any physical symptoms and/or chronic conditions you may be experiencing that persist despite medical intervention. Now consider any possibility of an emotional root to this pain. Are there past or present emotional responses or experiences you haven't allowed yourself to process? Are you holding onto old narratives that are hurting you? (Example from above: "It could be worse.") What might be some possible sentences you could replace those with? (Example: "It is exactly how it is.")

Real: The Rising

"I know for a fact that rock bottom is the beginning of newness. It hurts and it's painful and then there's the waiting, where you don't know what the hell is going on and you don't think any of it is going to make any sense and then there's the rising."
- Glennon Doyle

Great clarity and answers came through taking one small step at a time toward those tiny nudges—to gain the trust of the small inner voice and intuition I had left inside, to learn to trust *myself*.

The next pages don't contain the best medications I was prescribed or the supplements that line my cupboards, though I no longer have shame in finding help with both. The real truth is that taking care of my body with nourishing food, supplementing with vitamins and minerals that are lacking, and moving my body, are an integral part of maintaining physical and emotional well-being. *But* I am neither physician or nutritionist. In my experience, decisions about what pharmaceuticals to take will be the first bits of advice given to most seeking answers and guidance from traditional medicine and psychology. These needs are highly individual. It is up to each of us to maintain our authority in this area, not settle for doctors that aren't the right fit, do our own research, and determine what best suits our individual needs with the help of the medical professional(s) *we choose.* Likewise, dietary and exercise tolerances and needs are not one-size-fits-all. I argue that there are certain inflammatory foods we can all benefit from drastically limiting or eliminating entirely (looking at you refined sugar and artificial sweeteners); however, what foods best serve the functions of our bodies depends on our own, unique body. The research and recommendations seem to be ever-evolving, making this even trickier. I'd gladly tell you what I can and can't eat, what my body does and does not tolerate, but my body is not yours.

Medicine, nutrition, and exercise are the strong foundation of my health. That should not go without saying. They were the first answers I sought, and there is ample information and opinion out there to sift through concerning it all. A lot! Readily available. Easily Googled. I'm still learning and sifting and experimenting and growing and changing in all of the above. What's important, in my humble opinion, is that I know they are my foundation and I continue to take care of my body, mind, and soul by doing the best I can with each given what information I have at the time. Except, when I don't. In that case, I extend myself some much-needed grace and get back on track as soon as possible.

There are other tools that I stepped and stumbled into, in that search for myself and emotional healing, that I've later learned *also* have extensively researched, medical evidence for physical healing as well. These took a little more time and much more digging to find.

The next pages contain stories of how searching for emotional health, working to live a life of purpose and meaning, also (and often unknowingly) led me down a path to physical healing. I don't, can't, even separate them now—the physical, spiritual, and mental/emotional bodies. They are all one. So it went for me—first the pain, then the rising. Over and over again.

—

Invitation:

What are you already doing today to love and nurture your body, mind, and/or spirit? Alright! Celebrate that. What is one thing you'd like to make time for, something that would love and nurture your body, mind, and/or spirit? (Feel free to do some Internet searching before answering this question, if you'd like.) Plan for it—when, where, and how are you going to make it happen? How many days a week would you like to practice this? Do you need to let your family know that you'll be off-limits during the time you've set aside? Do you need to ask for help and support to remove some obstacles in making your plan a reality? You may be surprised at just how much the people who love you want you to do what's best for *you. Or* you may need to be prepared to do it anyway, with or without their support. You can make this happen!

Real: Truth

"So you decide to use life to free yourself. You become willing to pay any price for the freedom of your soul. You will realize that the only price you have to pay is letting go of yourself." - Michael A. Singer, The Untethered Soul

It is all connected—the physical body, the emotional body, the spiritual body—they are all energetically connected. That began to sink in through repeated trips to the chiropractor. This connection gave the words I said and thought great power. When I told my spiritual or emotional-self something, my physical body heard it. After enough repetition of unconscious thoughts, my body started to believe it, too. It also meant that my body kept a memory of all that I had been through, regardless of how hard I tried to or thought I could forget it.

The truth, the *whole* truth, that could set me free from the chains of depression pulling me into darkness; from the autoimmune disease diagnoses I had found validation in—it all had to come to light. The truth is, that the same parents that abandoned me when they were hurting and lost, were the ones that had an undeniable love for me for the many years before. She was the mom that made me the strawberry flavored milk, poured the sweet cream over sliced fresh peaches in a bowl just for me, handmade my Halloween costumes, and asked me if the dips in the dirt roads "tickled my tummy." He was the dad that took me out bumping through the fields, while I sat on the seat beside him, to check cattle in the early morning hours, tried to make my friends laugh, and cried over any harm he brought to animals. They were the parents who had cared for me, loved me, created a home, started family traditions, and nurtured me for so many years.

Those loving, nurturing parents were also the same people who emotionally and physically abandoned me when I was eleven, twelve, thirteen, fourteen, fifteen, sixteen, and seventeen. The first people to teach me about love were the first to teach me about fear and pain and loneliness. Regardless of how long I denied the truth of my past, or whether or not my parents acknowledged, understood, or discussed it, it would not be changed. It was there within me. My body knew it, had always known. It held the memory of all that had happened.

Walking through all of the pain was that much trickier given the contradictions of my past. Reconciling the mom and dad who both cared for me and hurt me would be the most difficult and most important work in becoming physically and mentally healthy. But I hoped for what was at the other end of that path, however long and arduous it may be. That hope pulled me up and pushed me into making just the next step, one at a time.

—

Invitation:

What if it's the contradictions of life that actually make life worth living? Life is, after all, full of long, winding, bumpy roads and straight, smooth, nicely-paved ones. Life is hard work *and* it's play. Life is sweet *and* it's bone-crushingly painful. It's both. It's all of the above all at once. Most often, people are too—good and bad, right? Consider any dichotomous thinking you may be holding onto. Is there anything you might be seeing as black and white, that's really some shade of gray? *Or* could it be black and white at the very same time? How might choosing to see the contradictions in past or present circumstances help you reconcile, accept them, and move forward? Journal your insights.

Real: Voices

"Prophecy is an animating stream that threads through all that is. The nonverbal language of this flow is possibility—the possibility of bringing forth new forms of life; the possibility of taking the next step on a journey; the possibility of another exodus. The prophetic stream speaks to all creation in its own language, exclaiming the vocabulary of potential…the potential to evolve, to expand in awareness, to grow in relationships." - Rabbi Nahum

Where I was headed, where I wanted to go, who I wanted to become, those things were not a destination, that was becoming clear. There would be no arriving. I learned this through my own trial and error, thinking time and again that I'd done it—mastered that issue, moved on from that feeling, evolved past that way of being. What I learned was that it was rarely that simple. It was much more about developing a practice that allowed me to be fully present and centered so that my actions, behaviors, and next choices were in alignment with the callings of my soul, with taking just the next step in trust. It was a journey with no end. I saw that now.

For so many years I built layers around my darkness, developed coping skills for functioning in society while avoiding my pain, habituated the addictions of people-pleasing and perfectionism that allowed me to numb myself from dealing with what I might find if I took a true look within. Yet here I was, placing all of what I'd hidden away inside in front of me to taking an honest look. I didn't want to stay here forever. That was the point. I was so tired of being stuck that I needed to find a way out. That's a journey, right? That's the word for it, right (even if it's an overused word)?

This journey into the wilderness of the depths of my soul was mine alone. That's why it's called the wilderness. I wasn't the first. Stories of people heading off into the wilderness to find themselves, to heal themselves, to transcend their current situation have been passed down for generations. Our most ancient texts contain them. "The only way out is through" no longer felt like such a platitude. I could ask for help. I could let those I cared about in close enough to understand, in hopes of support and encouragement. The work though, I had to do that on my own.

Here's the thing about the wilderness, it's unknown. By definition, it is a vast, isolated, and undeveloped space. Deciding to step into the wilderness is scary, metaphorical or not. Our limbic system, that fight or flight part of our nervous system, is inherently averse to this very idea. Our evolutionary survival is based on the ability to control our reality, our present life, and the path in front of us. Without this control, our ancestors most likely died in the jaws of some animal with really large fangs. The wilderness of our ancestors is not the wilderness of today. This figurative wilderness allowed me to step into the unknown while still enjoying the comforts of central heating and grocery store shopping. It sounds pretty pampered, but it was my scariest choice yet.

Journeying into and through this wilderness required ignoring that fear within, allowing myself to be called out into the unknown. It was there in the unknown that I'd find adventure and authentic aliveness, just like the wild self of my childhood. It is also where I'd find, just as I had as a child, uncertainty and vulnerability . Taking that step required a true act of faith and trust.

For me, this next step required not only placing faith and trust in the energetic spirit that flows through all things but developing faith and trust in myself—my intuition, my desires, my needs. I had lost all of that, if I ever had it in the first place. To find it required the simplest of actions over and over again, not easy but simple.

I still had all the old narratives playing on repeat in my mind. That scared naysayer within sounded like:

What if you fail?

What if you're wrong?

This is just selfish and self-indulgent.

What if your liberation hurts someone else?

What if they don't like you anymore?

Moving beyond that voice required two things. First, a realization that I was separate from that voice in my head, that I existed with or without that voice. If I was not that voice—the endless racket in my mind—then who was I? That was the second requirement, finding the me within that was independent of the narratives my mind had created in an attempt to protect me. Listening to that voice worked for me for a time. It had gotten me this far, but it was clear it was not working any longer.

There was another voice, a quieter one that didn't feel the need to compete with the blabbermouth or fill up all the empty space. Perhaps it was less of a voice and more of a feeling or a hunch, a guide or just curiosity. It never attempted to lay out the whole plan in front of me like an architect's blueprint. It never pleaded with me or tried to argue or convince. It was easy to miss. I didn't even really know or understand what I was hearing or listening to at first. I just knew something within me was leading me to the next step, just the one. I knew the only way to develop faith and trust in myself and in this divine spirit was to take that next step. So I did. I began taking just one next step at a time, without expecting anything from it. If there was a curiosity that wouldn't go away, I stepped toward it. If there was something that made me feel really scared, I stepped a little closer. If there was a voice in my head saying I could fail or people would judge me or I would waste my time or my money or there's no way I'd be perfect at it right away, I took one step in that direction.

This was not, is not, a pretty process. It wasn't, isn't, easy. There were a lot of tears involved, like the ugly cry kind of tears that made things come out of my nose, too. The tears came when I let the anger rise. They came when I not only remembered and acknowledged the whole truth to myself but shared it with those I trusted. They came when I had difficult conversations, conversations about not knowing myself; about the steps I needed to take to get to know myself; about what I wanted; about what I didn't want; about what needed to change for me to feel safe and free; about setting boundaries in relationships; about holding those boundaries or walking away. I said before that the wilderness is an uncertain and vulnerable place, and I repeat it now. Uncertain. Vulnerable. Tears were shed when I made mistakes. Mistakes are a prerequisite to learning and growth. Knowing how to redefine relationships in a way that allowed me to be true to the authentic self I was just beginning to discover was hard and hurtful and times. I didn't always get it right. I still don't.

I learned to replace the old narratives with new ones. Instead of letting that voice within say, *What if you fail?* when I tried new things in attempts at self-discovery, I told myself, *You will fail, sometimes.* Risk involves failure, doesn't it? Risk also involves adventure and excitement and authenticity and sometimes even reward. Instead of saying, *What if you aren't perfect at it right away?* I let myself say, *You'll probably screw this up at least a few times before you figure it out.* I gave myself permission. When I heard myself saying, *What will other people think?* I reminded myself, *What other people think about me and what I'm doing is really none of my business.*

Have you heard that classic Brené Brown quote about taking advice from people? She says, "If you're not in the arena also getting your ass kicked, I'm not interested in your feedback."

This quote is based on a Theodore Roosevelt speech that I already knew well, one that got me through many trying moments as a teacher:

> "It is not the critic who counts: not the man who points out how the strong man stumbles or where the doer of deeds could have done better. The credit belongs to the man who is actually in the arena, whose face is marred by

> dust and sweat and blood, who strives valiantly, who errs and comes up short again and again, because there is no effort without error or shortcoming, but who knows the great enthusiasms, the great devotions, who spends himself for a worthy cause; who, at the best, knows, in the end, the triumph of high achievement, and who, at the worst, if he fails, at least he fails while daring greatly, so that his place shall never be with those cold and timid souls who knew neither victory nor defeat."

Brené goes on in explanation:

> "Perfect and bulletproof are seductive, but they don't exist in the human experience. We must walk into the arena—whatever it may be—a new relationship, an important meeting, our creative process, or a difficult family conversation—with courage and the willingness to engage. Rather than sitting on the sidelines and hurling judgment and advice, we must dare to show up."

For perhaps the first time in my adult life, I decided to honestly, vulnerably show up as my truest, most authentic self, regardless of the opinions of others. That helped, too. It wasn't easy. I did screw up. I wasn't elegant or perfect or adept, although I never really was in the first place. I just allowed myself to live under the illusion that I might appear to be for my own false sense of safety and security. I chose to find the lessons in the failures and the mess-ups; to make myself vulnerable and have tough conversations; to live from a place of authenticity; to take just the next step in trust and in faith—in The Universe that was guiding me through my intuition—that it would lead me to the next, right step. And it did.

—

Invitation:

Can you hear your fear? What is it telling you—truth or lie? My experience tells me that fear is usually a liar. Fear is a deceptively cozy room, but it's not a nice place to live. It's not where you go to make decisions. What is one thing you're curious about, something you want to do or try or say or learn? What is one step you can take, you will take, even if you fail? Write a plan to take action. Remember, failure is one of life's greatest teachers.

Real: Trigger

"If you never heal from what hurt you, you'll bleed on people who didn't cut you." - Unknown

My oldest daughter began to near the age at which I'd experienced the trauma I'd been hiding and denying since its occurrence, at the same the time I found myself on the couch without purpose or hope for any future. In retrospect, this was no coincidence.

The memories of the wild I hung onto and experiences I could remember from very early childhood, were ones of love and acceptance, memories in which all of my needs were met by the adults in my life. My younger sisters, who were born when I was seventeen and twenty-two, were cared for in a similar way when they were young and I was around to witness. This reinforced what I'd been taught and shown about how to be a mother to young children. I had a strong foundation that was matched by my motivation to be a stable caretaker in the lives of my own daughters in all the ways I knew best. This early stage of motherhood came naturally to me.

As my oldest daughter entered her tween years, edging closer and closer to her early teen-hood, I did not have a clear picture of what motherhood would look like at this stage. This was, after all, the age at which I began to experience the trauma in my own life that would lead to my eventual loss of hope and desire to move forward in life in middle age.

When the sincere desire to deal with my shit so that I could find the hope, joy, and beauty I knew I should be feeling for my life sank in; when I finally decided to look back so that I could look forward; when I found just enough energy to do it not for myself, but for my daughters; when I realized I had to make a conscious effort to end any cycle there might be so I wouldn't unconsciously continue it, only then was I able to begin examining my actions and behaviors. I saw the first tiny glimpses of myself from outside myself, rather than buried beneath mountains of self-loathing self-talk. I started noticing things.

I noticed that I wasn't able to freely give affection to my oldest child, while it came naturally and without reservation for my youngest. My first daughter was now a preteen struggling with finding her own way into maturity and becoming less affectionate herself. That was true, but there were times that she came in for a hug or sat near to me that I felt myself pulling back or pushing her away. I simply didn't know how to affectionately nurture my daughter at this age. Simply by growing and maturing, something she had no control over, my daughter became a trigger to the pain of unmet needs in my own adolescence that I had repressed. What a hard pill to swallow, given that my primary purpose for getting up each morning was to be a good mother and give my daughters what I thought was a good life. Noticing that my actions and behaviors toward my daughter in this difficult transition in her own life were not in line with the caring and loving person I had believed myself to be created even more negative self-talk. At first, I spiraled. I spewed hateful remarks at myself, about myself, within myself, about all my shortcomings. I was so mean. But then I noticed that talk within. Just that noticing was a giant step.

Observing my negative self-talk was a new skill for me. I knew about shame now, so I started to notice that those downward, seemingly uncontrollable spirals of vitriol were brought on by shame. I observed the way that felt in my body—hot, overwhelming pressure in my chest and face, behind my nose and eyes. I understood that this shame would only grow if I continued to hide it away. In a desperate attempt to rid myself of these terrible feelings and unaligned actions as quickly as possible, I started to let myself feel them. If I felt like crying, I let that happen without trying to control it. That was all at first. I just let feelings rise, noticed them, noticed how they felt in my body, and noticed what precipitated them. Then slowly, I began to share them. I didn't shout them from rooftops, but I shared them with my husband and my daughter when I thought it would help her to understand me better.

One morning, I sat in a chair opposite my husband in our office and told him about what was going on in my head and heart and soul. I let him know that sometimes I heard myself saying the most horrible things like,

You're a terrible mother.

You're crazy.

Your kids will hate you someday.

I hate you.

I HATE you!

You don't even realize how crazy you are.

How could you have possibly thought you'd be a good mother or could have raised healthy children to grown into healthy adults?

One afternoon, after we completed a guided visualization at my husband's insistence (He'd heard it modeled by a coach on a podcast.)—one that was meant to end in an inspired vision of the beautiful future we were working to create together and reveal our innermost dreams and desires and the people in our lives that would be there the whole way—I came to another realization. I could picture myself on a stage in front of a room full of people as I was supposed to, but there was no one that I loved in the crowd or anyone that loved me. I couldn't even picture my own daughters or husband in my life years down the road. I found it impossible to imagine those I loved and cared for, loving and caring for me as I aged. I cried and cried as I told my husband all the things I realized through that visualization. It didn't elicit feelings of warmth or clarity or anticipation for the future I was creating, as intended. It showed me that I hadn't pictured a future for myself at all, that years of living in survival mode through trauma as a pre-teen and teen, then years of being told that I had serious health conditions that would dramatically decrease my life expectancy and the quality of my life, left me with no vision of my future at all. I didn't expect to live until late in life. I didn't expect to be in good health if I got there. I didn't think I deserved or would have the means to actually reach for dreams and accomplish them, so I just quit dreaming completely. And the most heartbreaking truth of all that came from that visualization, my fear that my daughters would not find enough love for me to be there in the end, whatever the end might be. It was heartbreaking. It was dramatic and emotional, but I was noticing. Not just that, I was allowing the emotions to come, feel them without suppressing them, and find faith and trust to share them.

Only after all of that, could I begin asking questions. Why was I feeling this way? Why was I talking to myself like this? Where did it come from? What could I do to change the narrative deep within me?

There was never a clear outline of steps to get from the darkest moment of the soul to a place of hope and peace and joy again. That never came. Yet, I knew that if I continued asking questions, continued praying, continued searching for answers, and continued taking action in trust, the next step would always come to me. There might be mistakes. It might not look pretty or perfect, but for the first time, I would keep stepping forward regardless.

—

Invitation:

What patterns might you possibly be repeating unconsciously in your relationship(s)? You don't have to repeat generational narratives. It starts with noticing. First, notice the behavior/feeling, without judgment or attempting to hide or change it. Let that feeling pass completely through your body, noting what it feels like in your body, without judging, changing, or trying to suppress it. Then, notice what precipitates that behavior, in the same way, bringing your thoughts and resulting actions into your consciousness. Now, make a decision and a plan for how you'd like to move forward. This change will most likely require leaving space—time between what makes you feel triggered and your response to that trigger. How can you plan for this? I don't need to tell you to journal your thoughts anymore, do I?

Real: Release

"Of course it hurts when it comes up. It was stored with pain, it's going to release with pain. You have to decide if you want to continue to walk around with stored pain blocking your heart and limiting your life. The alternative is to be willing to let it go when it gets stimulated. It only hurts for a minute, and then it's over."
- Michael A. Singer, The Untethered Soul

Because I never allowed myself to feel the pain and trauma, to feel and experience it in the moment, I never allowed it to pass through and be on its way. I coped the only way I knew at the time, ignoring it, pretending it never happened, denying my own feelings and experiences. In doing so, I didn't protect myself at all. I just held all the experiences so close that they remained stuck there inside.

Each time I shut someone out, hid myself away, built another facade, perfected a little more, I relived the old pain. Every time some event or some person or some setting triggered what I thought I'd forgotten, I relived it again. Stored pain equals reliving that pain over and over again.

Releasing the painful experiences I continued to feel because I'd built an existence upon trapping them within, meant I'd have to finally feel them, fully. By acknowledging them, confronting what I was hiding from, I was then able to release them. It was possible to feel these things, to be honest about what I'd been through and how it made me feel, and then let that feeling be on its way. In doing so, I could separate myself from the pain and fear and trauma and begin to see my truest self.

I was not my experiences. I was not my fears or my pain or even my thoughts. I was the being apart from all of those things. I was the one that observed all of it. The true me was the same soul that existed in the wild and the city, the same one that was still there under all of the armor I'd built around myself. I was there beneath all of those things that had happened around and to that little girl that she couldn't control.

The more I was able to access this inner observer, the one noticing all of the thoughts and happenings, without clinging to or trying to control any of it out of fear, the more freedom I was able to find.

Freedom felt like truth. Truth was like a deep breath, an exhale of a breath held for so long. Truth needed no explanation, no convincing. It was just a deep knowing. I began to feel who I was underneath it all. There was an intuition there, one that I could trust and act upon without checking for the approval of others first. A worthiness began to rise up, an undeniable right to be present with my own desires and callings that were valuable enough to be pursued.

Freedom and truth and intuition and worthiness weren't always present. Sometimes I still attached to the racing thoughts and acted upon them, to convince or seek the approval of others. Then I'd find it again. I would separate myself from my thoughts and what I perceived as the thoughts of others. I could come back to that observer behind all of the neuroses passing by. Then I could feel the little nudgings in the right direction again. I never had all the steps laid out clearly in front of me at once, but I could find just the next step, however small. I learned to take that step with a bit more confidence each time, gaining faith and trust in myself. The fear was still there, but I did it anyway.

The taste of freedom kept me coming back for more, in spite of how hard it was to face what I had hidden; in spite of how vulnerable it made me feel; in spite of the fear of what others might think; in spite of knowing that I'd fail and make mistakes; in spite of knowing that I'd lose some things I had been clinging to for so long, knowing that some of those things might even be people. I kept taking those small steps then, and today, one at a time, in spite of it all.

I knew that freedom makes the whole messy trip worthwhile.

—

Invitation:

Have you been mistakenly clinging to unpleasant experiences by refusing to let yourself feel them in the moment or after they happen? Did you think that by shoving them aside and moving on quickly, you were coping in a healthy way by not dwelling on negativity? What possible experiences might you have refused to let yourself "feel"? In doing so now, feeling them fully then letting them go, might you free up some space within for something new?

Real: Release - A Story

"We die all the time. I'm not the kid I was. That kid is dead. Your cells die every few days so new ones can be born. Let the past die, because it's gone. It doesn't exist. This is the only moment." - Deepak Chopra

I returned to that mountain—the cabin in the woods—where I'd died to myself not long before. I came back alone this time, in an effort to do the work of building a foundation of the woman I would become, for my daughters, for myself.

Sitting by the window, fourteen thousand foot peaks in the distance and hummingbirds nearby, I slowly started to let the stories come up, all the feelings and experiences I'd suppressed and denied for so long. Somehow, despite these actions, I'd never really forgotten them at all. At least some were still there, deep within me. In hiding them away, I'd actually just held them tightly, as though each was its own cherished gift worth saving. Only they weren't cherished gifts, they were that proverbial box of darkness that I'd unknowingly held so close to my heart all these years.

In hiding it away, I'd allowed that darkness to become one of the deepest parts of me, as much so as any light I held within. I didn't know that I could let it pass through me. No one taught me that then. No one showed me that I could experience something, in all it's fullness, dark and light—feel it, name it, talk about it—then let it pass right on through. They didn't know either—my mom, my dad, my brother. They didn't know that it's the denial, the attempts at hiding it away, the refusal to talk about what's happened, what's happening—that allows it to burrow a home, deep and dark, within. None of us knew that in all of our efforts to control the damage by denying the truth, we actually allowed it to cut that much deeper into our souls. It's only in acknowledging our experiences and a willingness to surrender fully to them in the moment, that we're able to release them completely. Through surrender, we are free.

I began to allow myself to feel all the things I'd hidden away, one at a time. As they came up from within, I let them pass—painfully—right on through. Why it would surprise me that this would be a painful process, I'm not sure. Each time a new memory presented itself, the dull ache and heaviness that took over would catch me off guard. It only makes sense that these painful and fearful memories held within would come forth with pain and fear again. My natural instinct, human instinct, is to run from or fight these experiences. That's what I'd gotten so good at doing for so long. That reaction was no longer serving me.

I'd hear that voice inside once again saying, *What is wrong with you? I thought you got over this and moved on already. A stronger person would have by now. You're weak. You're a fraud.* That cruel voice that for so long I'd thought was my deepest self—an insecure, self-critical mess—I began to recognize it. I thought I might know better now. I learned to sit back behind that voice now, to separate myself from it. I became able to listen to the nasty voice that needed to sling insults my way, without attaching to it or identifying with it.

Oh! There you are, I'd say back. *I hear you.*

My need to move forward with my life and move on to the true callings of my soul were so much greater than any ease, comfort, or familiarity I found in staying stuck any longer. I was ready for something new. That didn't mean it wasn't scary or hard. It was scary. It was difficult. But it was simple—listen to that voice, allow the fear to rule, stay stuck, OR love myself enough to move through the fear and pain despite the voice.

That day on the mountain, I let myself feel it—all of it. I felt it rise within me as the tears spilled over. More came, and I didn't suppress them as my first instinct told me to. More tears came then, still more. I was scared and uncomfortable—uncertain—so I asked for help.

"Help me get it all out right now," I prayed. "You take it!" I called to The Source of all I knew. "I don't want it anymore. I don't want to carry the shame and fear and anger and darkness of this man I've hated for so long with me anymore. If I'm going to do this, I don't want to do it again. Help me release it all now. Please? I *need* your help."

I walked down the mountain until I met the river that flowed perpendicular to it. It flowed full and fast with winter snowmelt, mirroring the emotions gushing forth from inside me. I didn't know what to do, so I turned and walked farther. I just kept walking, on and on, until I found a spot of rocks hidden from the road. I sat there by the Arkansas river in silence, staring at the rushing water meditatively, Mount Harvard in the landscape behind it. The whole time tears ran down my cheeks, escaping under the rims of my sunglasses, soaked up by the sleeve of my sweatshirt gloved over my fist as I wiped them away.

I'd walked so far and sat by the river for so long, let so many tears spill out of my face, leaking out with breathless sobs, as though they were pushed from deep inside. It was so ugly—such an ugly cry—but this final surrender was beautiful, too. This final moment of trust that I felt, that if I let myself really feel what was coming up within me—if I let myself experience it fully at that moment—I could trust that I wouldn't get lost in it. I could trust that I wouldn't be stuck there forever; that it wouldn't consume me entirely; that there wasn't something wrong with me; that help would come if I needed it, if I asked; that in feeling the depth of the experience I'd tried so hard for so long to forget, I'd release it into the vast ether beyond and not lock it within. I trusted that I could finally let it go, once and for all.

So I let myself cry for the little girl that had so much taken away from her so long ago. I cried for all that was stripped from her and all the growing up she had to do at such a young age out of necessity. I wept for the incomplete adult she'd stitched together because she didn't know any better, only doing the best she could at the time. I cried still, for the faulty coping skills she'd clung to out of survival that were so difficult to let go of now, in mid-life. I allowed all the tears to come, no longer seeking to control them.

And then, in the very next moment, they were gone. They were done. No more tears rose from within. None. So I did the only thing I could think to do—I got up from that cool, shady slab of granite by the river and began to walk right back from where I'd come, retracing the steps that had gotten me there. It was only then, after all of that, that help did come. A twenty-something rafting guide pulled up right beside me in his rickety, old eighteen-passenger van pulling an empty trailer. He must have been on his way to retrieve the rafters and guides further down the river, but he slowed to a stop as he asked me, "Need a ride?" His shaggy, sun-bleached hair escaping from beneath all the edges of his cap.

"No, but thanks for the offer," was the answer that came from my mouth without thought or contemplation. "I'm walking here on purpose."

And I was.

Much has struck me since that offer of help by the river, on the way back up the mountain, that day and in the weeks to follow. There have been many unexpected gifts of letting go, releasing the darkness I'd been unknowingly clinging to made room for light to enter.

Gratitude was the first to find its way in, right there on that dirt road as I once again ascended the hill. I had more room to be grateful for all I had. I found gratitude for the love I found for myself now; for the ability and trust to ask for help; for the help granted; for the honor found in living this life and in coming through the pain and struggle; for the ability to do it again. I was grateful for all the Divine inspiration that kept leading me to just the next step in designing the life of my soul's destiny.

Later it would occur to me that only through letting go was I able to reach a deeper clarity as well. I realized that at least part of the anger that kept coming up was anger toward a man who I thought had stolen so many things so precious to me. I had, to that point in life, been raised by a wild woman—a mom so full of life that it burst from her in contagious laughter. My mom was the kind of wild woman that would lift me into the shopping cart at the grocery store. Then she'd run through the parking lot at full speed while pushing the cart. Finally, when we were going fast enough, she'd put one foot firmly on the bar between the wheels at the base of the cart and raise the other in the air behind her as the cart glided between parked cars, quickly releasing its momentum. We'd laugh and smile together, and my mother, the wild woman that she was, would actually yell, "Weeeee!" with abandon, without fear of judgment.

The story I had created and held onto for so long was that this sick man who medicated himself with alcohol and cruelty and abuse, stole that woman from me. He stealthily stole pieces of her, bit-by-bit, little-by-little over time, so that she didn't understand what was happening. He took this wild, unfettered woman that I called mom, and turned her into a scared little girl with no friends, family, or connections of her own that could breathe life into her. He stripped all that he thought could rescue her away, including me, consciously or unconsciously, until all she was left with was him and an unattainable hope that she could save him from himself somehow. That would never happen. The truth is, I had no way of knowing the full truth then—her truth, his truth—and I have no way of knowing the full truth now. It was trying to understand it, name it, define it, create villains and victims, cloak it under shame and fear and denial—that led to holding it so tightly for so long. Releasing it was the opposite of that.

Releasing the strange, disjointed bits I'd been strangling deep within for so many years, mistakenly thinking I was moving on and not letting it get the better of me, made space for reflection and clarity. I could see I'd actually been clinging to anger, too. Mad is the wrong word for such deep-seated anger that had been brewing for so long—boiling and bubbling and reducing it into a concentrated, thick, tarry mass. This wasn't just mad, it was pissed maybe, but not just pissed-off, no that wasn't strong enough either. Rage. Rage was more like it. Rage for the man, the men—the alcoholics my mother loved—that stole the innocent child of my soul, everything that was good and wild in me, and left me with only a box of darkness in its place. Rage for the mother who let it happen, who let him, both men, reduce her to a shell of what she had been. Rage for the father who was not there to notice. Rage for the mother and father who blindly allowed it to happen, not just that, actively participated in the dismantling of a family and life that had embodied that goodness. I had been carrying around a rage for a mother that could let all of that happen without realizing it and without ever saying the words, "I'm sorry."

There is no way to reconcile the person I had become—the one I let the world see—and a being full of rage. The two did not go together. They were no match. If I were to give my friends and family one of those matching memory games from childhood but replace the cards with pictures of my outsides and insides, none of them, not one (myself included) would match the outer me I'd fashioned to control everyone's perception of me, with the dark rage that had festered within me for years. Everyone playing that game would lose.

That night on that mountain by the river, when I let that rage flow up and out and through me in tears and sobs, I opened up a space within. I allowed that space to fill with light and clarity. That light revealed and released that rage I'd kept unknowingly inside me. That's all it took, an acknowledgment of its existence, and it too flowed up and through and out. I was full of rage and I wasn't even conscious of it. Now I am, and that rage is gone. In its place is a stillness. That stillness allows me to observe more and judge less, to see my mom with a little more understanding and a lot less expectation. I can empathize with the scared child inside her that had so much stolen from her, too—the woman, the life, the family that she'd built then found slipping away from her. Letting it rise within me; letting myself feel it fully; allowing myself to name it, give it shape and form; allowing those feelings to express themselves—that is the only way to let them move on.

—

Invitation:

Are you finding it difficult to let go of the past, regardless of how hard you try? Who could you call on for help? If you pray or talk to God (The Universe, Source) try saying this, "You take it." Offer it up. Give it away. Let it go. Then release it in whatever way it needs to be released, without suppressing it in any way.

Real: Death Comes Knocking

"It may be the luckiest and purest thing of all—to see time sharpen to a single point, to feel the world rise and shake you hard, insisting that you rise, too, somehow. Some way. That you come awake and stretch, painfully. That you change—completely and irrevocably—with whatever means are at your disposal—into the person you were always meant to be." - Paula McClain, Love and Ruin

"I don't want this!" I remember crying out to my husband. "I don't want more drama or doctors or sickness."

After eight years of specialists, tests, medications, and diagnoses, what I once saw as permission and affirmation to slow down and take a break, became a prison. I had resigned myself, at some point, to the idea that my particular shade of autoimmune disease wouldn't allow me to go quietly in the night or take me when I was least expecting it. I developed this notion that I would pass, only after my body had eaten itself away into a crippled deformed version of my youthful self, not quickly, but slowly and painfully.

I quit my job and found ways to free myself and my days so that I could begin to live the life that I had left on my terms. Working on my mental and physical health had become a top priority. But I became complacent in many ways, too. I forgot the urgency of this matter of life. I had transitioned into a quieter life of settling, little by little. That's when death came for a much-needed visit.

Death spoke softly at first. It wasn't easy to speak at my eighty-five-year-old (maternal) granddad's funeral or bury him, but it came and went as a reminder of the cycle of life. Death kept coming. It took our dogs and our backyard-chickens. I watched and shed tears and said prayers of gratitude for all they had given us. Then Death came for my (maternal) Grandma and my (paternal) Granddad Joe all at once. Having missed any chance of closure or goodbyes with my Grandma (her passing was too quick for goodbyes), I was sure not to squander this opportunity with one of the greatest influences of my life.

To my benefit, the lessons death had been trying to teach me quietly, over and over again, came before I had to say goodbye to him. This allowed me to see the peace in that finality. It taught me that there was no regret when Death came for him, because there was no regret in how fully he chose to live his life—how true he was to the soul that shone inside him. There was a sadness, of course, at the realization that there'd be no more conversations or laughs shared. But there was no regret in letting his soul leave the body that could no longer contain him properly. And there was only gratitude in being able to witness and be a part of that final act of love.

I can thank Death for these repeated reminders that seemed to increase in frequency. I didn't fully note Death's gift until it came knocking even closer to home. That's when the realization of surrendering control and living in the present really sank in, after the cries to my husband of course. Just when I thought I had at least a slight grasp on my own health—a narrow road to maintaining it—I got a call from my rheumatologist telling me that the echo-cardiogram I had that morning showed that I had pulmonary hypertension.

My first response was to brush this off, as:

1. I had no idea what pulmonary hypertension was, and
2. I felt better than I had in years—in all ways.

The monkey mind—the Buddhist term for the unsettled, restless mind, as though jumping through thought—grabbed hold of me eventually, and it didn't take much Googling to realize that this would both dramatically decrease my lifespan (Google said it would most likely be less than three years after diagnosis) and *dramatically* increase my health care expenses until heart failure began and the end came.

Death got really loud and right up in my face, like a drum keeping the base beat so close to my face I could feel its vibration. After the obligatory freak-outs and fearful internal conversations, something new took over. I felt an unwavering sense of calm—centeredness and internal knowing I had never felt before. I knew that my soul was just fine. I was worthy just as I was. There was no more striving or proving necessary. I *knew* that my daughters and my husband would be okay. They would be sad and grieve, but they were amazingly resilient and powerful humans that would continue to be so with or without me. I knew that I would be okay, too, if I had to go. Not okay if I was living my life from the couch surrounded in a cloud of darkness, but okay if I was choosing to live my life to its fullest. Death taught me that I was a soul, not the body that carried that soul around. If I allowed my soul to come forth and shine its light, to listen to its calls for action, if I gave everything that my soul had to give while I was in this form, then death too would be okay.

This was my next call to action. This was my next hint to shed yet another layer. Was I living the life that my soul was put here to live? No. Not yet, but I knew that was now my mission.

After so many years of becoming a people-pleasing, no-rocking-the-boat perfectionist, I still had little idea of what my soul's gift actually was. My inner voice and intuition were so quiet and meek after all of my years of silencing them. It was still there though, and my work now was in finding that inner voice and intuition again—to gain its trust by acting on it, by allowing it to get louder and bolder in its requests of me. I would take action, one small step at a time.

—

Invitation:

If you knew you just had today, how would you live it? That's the call, right? There are no guarantees, diagnosis or not. What is the thing calling from within your soul that won't go away—the curiosity or hunch or dream or wish or thing you're most enthusiastic about? What is one step, even the smallest one, you can take in the direction of that calling, today?

Real: I'm Not Afraid To Die

"It is truly a great cosmic paradox that one of the best teachers in all of life turns out to be death. No person or situation could ever teach you as much as death has to teach you. While someone could tell you that you are not your body, death shows you. While someone could remind you of the insignificance of the things you cling to, death takes them all away in a second." - Michael A. Singer, The Untethered Soul

Unmistakably, the *truth* of much of what was in me, and most certainly the wild, was all wrapped up in the package of a single man—Otto Joe, my Granddad. He was founder and CEO of that wild place tucked into the arroyo and settled into the sand, and likewise the wild place in my heart.

He didn't actually homestead the place we would call The Ranch. I learned that many years later when writing the eulogy for his funeral. That fact didn't concern me. He was the foundation of my truth within.

Joe wore a cowboy hat, not as a piece of a costume, but as a piece of who he was. Below that, as part of his daily uniform, was always a short-sleeved, western shirt—the kind with shiny, pearl-colored snaps for buttons. Then he'd finish off with blue jeans and boots most days, especially on nice occasions. He was king of the catch-phrase in my book, with pithy comments like, "I wouldn't want to live anywhere else." and "I've never been to a day of work in my life, because I love what I'm doing," always at the ready.

Though I had many guides I'm grateful for along the way, many who intervened and influenced when desperately needed, he was the guide with the most succinct lessons all wrapped up into one, in his very own character: integrity trumps all; honesty is the only way; a good sense of humor can cure almost all that ails you; take care of what God gave you; hard work isn't hard at all when you love what you're doing; happiness can't be bought or given and stays with you no matter where you are; *everyone* deserves a fair shake; what's mine is yours; there's no better way to pass the time than with a good game of cards; there's no better place than right here. He made living simply and living right look easy, and would have argued with anyone who told him it wasn't.

There were struggles along the way and lessons that taught and shaped such a character of integrity, I'm guessing, but I wasn't really around to see those. Like most grandchildren, I was just around to see what had set after all the glue dried—in this case, to benefit from a firm foundation. Not just from him, but from my grandmother, too; both were often anchors in the commonly turbulent waters of my life that left me adrift. From the two of them, I learned how to fish, then how to clean and cook that fish. From Grandmother, I learned about embroidery, gardening, cooking, and all the best mystery novels. From Granddad, how to bait a hook, drive a stick-shift, check cattle, and the very best card games. Their home was always a landing place, where I was always welcome and always felt safe and loved. They taught me about love.

This is why it's such a surprise to me that one of Granddad's greatest lessons would be in his death. In his retirement, my granddad maintained, bought, and created many businesses. He met all of life with the vigor of someone years his junior. Despite this, the health issues of an aging body weren't beyond him.

In my college years, he had a heart attack and quadruple bypass with a subsequent pacemaker. Years later, while working in his shop, he would fall from a bucket he was perched on in place of a proper ladder and break a hip. And while his mind and soul remained young—pushing him to continue working, creating, doing, serving, and exploring the world—the physical organ that was his heart began to show signs that it wasn't up to the task. The aching hip that would never fully recover didn't help much either.

When his cardiologists let him know that his heart failure would not allow him to stick around much longer, he was able to talk one such doctor into installing an entirely new, bionic left ventricle. It seems clear now, that the tough, old dude saw this as another wild adventure he wasn't at all scared to go on.

In retrospect, I'm not sure he'd take that adventure again, but his new bionic heart did allow us to begin and practice the grieving process early with Granddad. Having the grateful surprise of him surviving the installation process of the LVAD, made the four years with him that followed time to be cherished. Granddad was never one for drama or to make a big deal of things, so grand gestures of sadness and devotion wouldn't have been fitting. I remember grieving him several times throughout those years, and still, he hung on, laughing and fishing as much as possible, though the weakness of his heart did tend to muffle that and his voice from time to time.

Then, just as spring turned to summer of his final year, we'd learn that an infection going from one of his leads (feeding the battery power to the device in his heart), was incurable. It was only a matter of time before that infection consumed him—two weeks to two months. He would go home to pass peacefully, using his powers of persuasion again to talk a local, small-town doctor into working with his big-city doctors to monitor him and administer the necessary medications with my grandmother's aid. Yet still, he not only hung on but appeared to thrive in the best way he could in this stage of life with his body.

He'd check cattle and do any errand or chore that required him driving his little, red flat-bed pickup around town or all over the plains of South Eastern Colorado and the connected portion of Kansas bearing the same resemblance. He drove and worked in his shop and played cards and drank a bit of wine and went on doing just as much as his body would allow until Christmas decorations started going up.

It was clear now, that the infection had entered his lungs. While the hope-front was in full force that Granddad would make a recovery and be out of the local hospital in time for holiday celebrations (he refused to be taken back to the hospital in Denver), something began to whisper to my heart.

Having just experienced the loss of my mother's mother without feeling the breath of the last goodbye, only a week before, I did not want to squander any such opportunity that may have been presenting itself at that moment. I made the little over two-hour trip down to see him the night that I heard. I visited him a couple of times, balancing my newfound desire and metamorphosis with becoming real and what I imagined to be my grandparents' desires to keep it low key and without drama.

Popping into his room that night as soon as I got there, I let them know that my surprise visit to the hospital was purely because "I had to come down to take care of some paperwork with Dad anyway." That wasn't real, but it was as real as I could muster at that moment. I kept it cool, the whole time wondering if these would be my last conversations with this man that was such a pivotal character in the entire arc of the story that was me.

The next morning, I came by for a brief visit, and found my granddad alone before my grandmother arrived that morning. Walking into the room, the strained breath in and out of his lungs filled the room, sounding like the very walls of his chest were fluttering with each attempt. He startled awake when I sat down on the hospital bed beside him, doing a poor job of sneaking in. He sat covered and partially inclined in the chair beside it. Out of regret at having woken him and a poor attempt at humor, I asked, "Are they torturing you again?" He tried to return the lightness with a laugh, but the strength of the pneumonia won, and the exhaustion that seemed to fill him so deeply cut his barely apparent laugh off too soon.

This turned out to be a gift, as the only thing left at that moment, humor and pleasantries having failed us, was real. I sat calmly and completely on the edge of that bed with its starchy hospital white linens, and let all the real of the moment seep in. Then I said the only real words I could find in that moment at time, the truest thing I could think to say.

"You did good, granddad. You did good."

The best part was the way he stared back at me, right in the eyes, like he let it sink in. Like he knew, too. Like we shared a secret of sorts at that moment that this might be the last, real conversation we'd have.

After a while, he'd answer back, "I think so. I tried. I really did."

Just then my grandmother came into the room and with her a fresh wave of hope and mustered enthusiasm for the day swept over the three of us—whether real or for the benefit of each other, I'm not sure. My granddad sat up a little straighter in his chair, his breath became clearer, and he spoke a little louder. We talked about the day and the weather and laptops and WiFi passwords and got everything lined out and everything straight and mentioned going home soon. We promised to hang in there and see each other at Christmas and New Year's.

I left the room alone, carrying with me a sense of sadness and closure all intertwined, but the real lesson I carried home was what life looked like when it was time to go—how a body appeared when it no longer served the expansiveness of the soul within it. A strange feeling enveloped me, as though it passed slowly from my head, down my body, and all the way over my feet, gently covering me with a sense of knowing. For the first time, while my granddad was still alive in the room behind me down the hall, a truth sank in. The truth was that death wasn't bad or scary, that it wasn't something to be afraid of or even to dread. The truth about death is that it's just a part of the process, part of living. Death could be sad, sure. It would be sad to no longer experience the vibrancy of Granddad's soul in person. I would mourn this loss.

One of the greatest lessons of becoming real for me happened in this moment, in the truth of knowing that death itself isn't the worst thing imaginable. My granddad's life made that really clear. He had lived his life fully. His soul had radiated so brightly and so clearly from him when he was truly living, that it became remarkably obvious when it could no longer do that. It was time for his soul to go when his body became such a poor vessel for it. His soul did not belong in that hospital gown in that chair with those tubes coming out of it in that small room down that long hallway with its shiny floor tiles that smelled of rubbing alcohol and bleach. It could no longer contain that soul, nor should it. That's not where it belonged anymore. I understood then. I would miss him dearly, but what would be truly heart-breaking would be to try to contain the essence of him within something so clearly ill-fitting any longer.

That day, I learned that death is not sad when it allows the liberation of an ever-expanding soul from its mortal body. Death is just the gift that enables the return to one's essence.

—

Invitation:

Is there someone in your life that has always been there to support you or someone whose example of life continues to inspire you? Who? What is it about them that most inspires you or that you feel most grateful for? Tell them! Call, write, text, meet them for coffee, it doesn't matter how, just let them know. If they've passed, speak it out into the vastness and assume that they can hear you. Now, what is at least one inspiration you can take from them to begin living the life you're meant to live?

Real: Dear Me - A Letter To My Thirteen-Year-Old Self

"We know what the world wants from us. We know we must decide whether to stay small, quiet, and uncomplicated—or allow ourselves to grow as big, loud, and complex as we were made to be. Every girl must decide whether to be true to herself or true to the world. Every girl must decide whether to settle for adoration or fight for love." - Glennon Melton, Love Warrior

Dear Darling Girl,

You are a fucking badass! You've found a way to survive this difficult time that's cut a valley right through the center of your soul. You've found a way through. You are a deeply emotional and feeling being. Empathy is your superpower. All of those tears you're crying, they'll be your gift someday. You'll find a way to use the pain and sadness you're locking away to make art and magic of your life. You'll use it to help empower others to do the same with their lives. Use your gifts, baby girl! Don't be afraid of them.

You have a vibrancy and energy that comes from deep within your soul. Your laugh spreads that light to those around you. When you lean into the full beauty of your authentic energy, you can light up a room full of souls and carry them right along with you. Don't be afraid of this power. Own your power!

You will take your time getting around to finding yourself, the you that you've gotten so good at hiding away for so long, but you'll get there. Be patient and love yourself the whole way.

Just so you know…

You are not your body.

You are not your mom or your dad or your brother or your sisters.

You're not your husband.

You're not even your own daughters.

You're not your illness or your diagnosis or your medications.

You are not your job.

You are not the approval you seek from others.

You are not your house or your car or your lawn full of dandelions.

You cannot be found or contained in the shoes on your feet, the make-up covering your face, or the clothes on your back.

You are the radiant light that shines deep within; the one behind all the lies you've told yourself; the one who watches all of it swirling and circling all around you; the one who's been there the whole time. Take all of the people you love and your possessions and labels away, and still, you'd find your soul glowing from that place inside. Let that light shine, beautiful girl. Let it shine!

—YOU

—

Invitation:

Write a letter to your younger self during your most difficult time. (You guessed this one, didn't you?) What can you say to that younger version of yourself that you know to be true now? What do you have to celebrate about how far you've come since then? Be your biggest cheerleader, your biggest supporter and encourager. Soak in all the *knowing* you have at this very moment, and put it on the page. You know what, don't be afraid to write it from a future version of yourself you're confident you'll become. All the better!

Real: Forgiveness

"I thought perfection was the glue of secure attachment. That rewriting the story was the hallmark of redemption. But when I stopped running from the mother I didn't want to be—when I forgave my mother for the narrative she unknowingly authored—I could finally give my son what he needed all along: my presence." - Ashley Abramson, Parenting in the Aftermath of Trauma

I've learned a few things about forgiveness in this process of pulling myself out of the pit that was rock bottom.

First, forgiveness is imperative to moving forward. I'm talking about true, deep, authentic forgiveness now. Not the superficial, "It's okay," I'd been faking my way through in the past. Without real forgiveness, I got stuck. I kept playing the same stories over and over in my head. This kept me in a cycle of disappointment, anger, regret, and self-deprecation. It's hard to keep faking it or picking yourself up off the couch with narratives that carry those themes playing on a loop.

Second, forgiveness is much simpler when someone asks for it. Through all of the years of being abandoned and left to fend for myself,

I realized that I'd perhaps gone a bit easy on my dad. Not that I was easy on him, really. There was plenty of passive-aggressive anger sent his way and a lot of shutting him out, but I did give him the benefit of the doubt more than I did my mom. This could possibly be attributed to many things—I spent more time with my mom; the pain of being hit with the shrapnel of her choices was much more frequent and at closer range; she was my mom, her love was meant to be unwavering and protective and fierce. It's possible I held what I saw as her transgressions against me to a higher standard unconsciously. The more I began to work on forgiveness, the more I began to realize that she'd never asked for it. I'm not even sure that she thought there was anything to forgive. We've still never spoken much about it.

It was much simpler to forgive someone who had cried to me begging for it; someone who carried with him a weight that I recognized, the weight of shame and regret for the decisions he'd made and the hurts he'd caused; someone who had spent so many years trying to make up for it; someone like my dad. I'm not saying that any of that is right or good or fair to anyone involved, but I am saying it made forgiveness easier. I had to learn how to forgive someone that didn't ask for it, who possibly didn't even know that their actions or inaction might require forgiveness. This proved to be much more difficult but no less necessary for my healing. I found the following quote from Meredith Rom of Rising Women Leaders to be true:

> "We could spend our whole lives waiting for someone to apologize or to take responsibility for how they hurt us before we decide to let go. But we've made someone else in charge of how and when we heal. If we truly want to break a cycle and heal, we have to forget about what the other person is or isn't doing and focus entirely on our own process."

Furthermore, forgiveness isn't a one-time thing. Forgiveness is not a battle to be fought and won so that you can move on and never look back. I've tried that, it didn't work. Forgiveness isn't a one-and-done.

Forgiveness is:

1. a way of living, a choice, to see flawed humans as just that, flawed.
2. an acceptance and trust that whomever we're forgiving did the best they could at the time.

I've learned that forgiveness is the exhale after a long, labored breath. I let it go, but like breath, I exhale it over and over again.

Ultimately, to forgive others meant learning to forgive myself first. It was first necessary to acknowledge that I was flawed and that I'd done the very best I could at the time with what I had and what I knew. Doing that allowed me to extend that same acknowledgment to my parents. It showed me that each time I judged and became angered at their choices and actions, I was doing the same to myself. Each time I did so, I was also reliving the painful memories of the past over and over again. Only through recognizing and accepting my own imperfections without judgment, could I extend the same to the imperfect humans my parents were. I learned how to forgive them by learning to forgive myself. Doing so was one step toward leaving the past behind.

After that, I was able to make clearer decisions about if and how I wanted to maintain those relationships in my life. As time went on, it became clear that much of my heartbreak had been created by unspoken and unmet expectations of what I thought a mother and father should be and do. Releasing those expectations brought a freedom to both relationships. I could control my own expectations and behaviors, nothing else. I put my efforts into showing-up as myself in relationship with them, any time and under any circumstance, regardless of their actions and behaviors. Conversely, I slowly learned to release any expectations I had of them at all, until eventually all I expected of them was to be themselves, whatever that was. That gave me the freedom to be in relationship with them while holding the boundaries I needed to maintain for my own health. It meant a lot less disappointment, too, by letting go of expecting, wanting, or needing things that were outside my control or that they simply couldn't give.

Exhaling forgiveness in this way, over and over again, cleared a space inside. That space leaves room for deeper breaths, newness, freedom, and all the light my soul had been crying out for for so long.

—

Invitation:

Forgiveness is some tough shit (I feel like it's okay to curse to add emphasis), am I right? Not like, you-forgot-to-call-me-on-my-birthday forgiveness, though that can be tricky, too. Like the, you-unknowingly-changed-the-entire-course-of-my-life forgiveness, or I-hate-you-I-hate-you-and-everything-you-did-to-me forgiveness. Big, big stuff. What if you tried taking a really deep breath, then on the out-breath you said (to yourself or aloud), "I let go." Then, do it again and again and again. When you've done it enough times that you feel yourself letting go, and you aren't in fight or flight brain any longer, consider forgiving yourself first. Consider forgiving yourself for any actions, behaviors, patterns, coping skills, numbing—anything—you've taken on or done as a reflection of someone else. Forgive yourself, one breath, one release at a time. Then do it again, over and over again, as many times as it takes. That's a good place to start.

Real: Shedding - The Dance Of In Between

What's with this back and forth,
  the ebb and flow,
  in and out?
I want to shed this skin,
  and leave it far behind.
It keeps dragging along,
  creeping behind me.
  I lose focus
  and it slips right back on again.
It feels worse this time,
  old, scaly, wrong.
  still, it clings,
  this past way of being.
Until I notice it's once again suffocating me,
  no longer stretching to contain my growth.
I shake and wriggle and tear it away
  one more time.
And I am free.
Again.

Invitation:

Do you notice yourself making progress—growing and changing—then regressing into old routines, habits, versions of yourself, or coping skills? Me too. Often this happens when I'm challenged or spend time with people who haven't been around much to witness my progression. I'll tell you, though you don't need my blessing, that it's okay. It's normal, even. Thank yourself for noticing. You might not have noticed not so long ago. Now thank yourself again for getting back up and trying it all again. How resilient! You'll persevere, indeed!

Real: Meditation

Oprah: There's a shack inside all of us.

William Paul Young: Yeah, and it's our own heart. It's our own soul. The process of transformation is not about becoming something that we are not. It's about unveiling what we were the whole time.

Oprah: So there's nothing to transform. There's just all of this to unveil. The process of uncovering becomes your own transformation.

- Conversation between William Paul Young (author, The Shack) and Oprah Winfrey, Super Soul Conversations

I left my job to relieve daily stress, yet, I quickly found myself in a familiar place. I cooked lots of healthy food. I no longer had the stress created by a job outside my home. Yet the physical pain in my body persisted and the stress and depression I was feeling deep within wouldn't go away. I tried to hide it, but it leaked out regularly in phrases like, "I'm too busy," or "I don't have enough time." My daily headaches were another continuous reminder that something was still up.

I didn't get there quickly, but I did begin to entertain the idea of working on my mental health. I didn't know that's what I was doing of course, but when I found the book *The Miracle Morning* by Hal Elrod, I was being nudged slowly in that direction. Unconsciously, I took it as a challenge to get even better at the perfectionist game and power ahead, full-steam, to achieve great things and really impress some people. Of course, I didn't even know I was seeking approval, of myself and others, at that point. That would come later.

I started meditating. It was one of the morning practices in Hal's book, after all, and I was going to do it right. I knew no other reason for meditating. I knew nothing about meditation's extensively researched health benefits. I just found an app on my phone, downloaded it, and followed the guided instructions to the best of my ability for as long as I could. I was going to be the best meditator…for at least four minutes every morning! Finally working up to ten minutes at a time was excruciating. I continued.

I remember the specific moment that the actual meaning of mindfulness, which had just been lip service to that point, truly sunk in. My youngest daughter, four-years-old at the time, and I were working at our first rental property. We were sprucing it up while my oldest daughter was at school and my husband was at work. During these moments, I often found it difficult to live in the present—simply noticing and focusing on exactly where I was, what I was doing, and what was happening around me. Meditation, still a very new practice to me, was just beginning to help with that. I didn't even know yet, that I was making slow and steady progress toward mindfulness. That gift gave me a new understanding that day, as I rolled paint up and down a tiny, cramped, kitchen wall to cover up the cigarette-smoke smell left behind. I let my mind wander to thoughts of the past (not a reminiscing with friends and loved ones, but wander in busy, hectic thought), and I heard thoughts of judgment, blame, regret, shame, and embarrassment. Not being present in the moment by letting my mind wander to thoughts of the past, only meant I'd overthink and create insecurities and self-doubt. That is not a good place to live in the mind. Then I started noticing that, just as quickly, my mind would alternate to thoughts of the future. What I heard from myself then was worry, fear, doubt, stress, anxiety. My mind went to feelings of scarcity (*I'm so busy. I don't have enough time.*) I was trying so hard to overcome—feeling that I had too much to do without hope of getting it all done. That's not a good place to live in the mind, either.

The brief, follow-the-leader style meditation practice I had was subconsciously teaching me where joy lives. I was just beginning to understand that joy lives in now. I started to notice that I found the most joy when I focused on only the present and let everything else go, knowing that it was okay if "now" isn't always joyful. But it was so much easier to find joy when I was truly present. Had I missed this gift of mindfulness meditation was giving me, I would have also missed the joyful moment between my daughter and our loyal dog. I would have been so caught up in stress, worry, and exhaustion with a long list of chores related to the new venture we were undertaking as a family, that I never would have heard her laughter from the stoop outside the propped-open front door just a few feet away from me. As I stood on that step stool reaching as high as possible with my roller brush soaked in beige-brown paint, I left the past, left the future, left them both behind. I got present. Only then did I hear a laugh that rang right from the heart of that little curly-haired, olive-skinned girl of mine. I stepped down and quietly toward the door to witness her enjoying a simple moment in the sun with her dog. I still remember it so clearly that it brings tears to my eyes. It was so beautiful in its simplicity, *so now.* I never would have stopped rolling my paintbrush long enough to hear the quiet giggle or go watch and snap a picture, had I not learned to bring myself back to the present moment through meditation.

I also would have missed the sincere joy on both my girls' faces as they willingly helped with the long list of chores we were undertaking at that house. They were not hindered by regrets of the past or worries of the future. Children really know how to live in the moment. They found ways to laugh and enjoy themselves as they went about their work. And I was truly present to notice it. That was enough of a carrot to keep me coming back for more with my meditation app.

Another layer, just barely beginning to peel back at the edges. Meditation would require a lot of continued practice, I would learn again and again. It wasn't a quick fix—not something I could figure out, master once, and move on. As with all of the mental and emotional well-being practices and work I was just beginning to dip my big, fat, clunky toe into it and it would take continued commitment to an effort of deep practice.

This led to finally considering entertaining the idea of trying yoga, also excruciating. My monkey mind was chattering up a storm.

You want me to hold this pose for how many more breaths? You've got to be kidding! Am I even breathing at all? Oh yeah, I must have forgotten.

Compared to the "high-intensity interval training" that allowed me to move quickly from one thing to the next and strengthen my ego with a fake sense of just how strong and powerful I was in one, quick, thirty-minute workout, yoga was hell. It took tiny steps of practice, bit-by-bit to finally gain an appreciation for what it had to offer.

The truth, learning to sit with my rushing mind, the incessant internal dialog my ego had built up around me to make me feel worthy and important, was tough. It took so long to realize there was even internal dialog at all. Then I had to observe what it was telling me, all those lies about being busy and not having enough time (or not enough money or whatever it wanted me to feel was lacking). I could finally recognize that meditation and yoga were so ridiculously difficult because my mind wouldn't shut up. Meditation and yoga allowed me to realize what my mind was constantly racing on about. Something like this...

I better hurry and get this meditation over with so I can get on with all the really important things I need to do today.

My kids and my husband need me to do all of these things for them so that they can do all of their really important things too.

I have so many really important things to do.

I'm really busy.

I don't have enough time to do it all.

I hope everyone sees how busy I am, so they know how little time I really have, so they realize I'm not lazy, so they know that if I'm not lazy I'm still a hard worker even though I don't have a real job anymore, so they know that I'm really a good person.

Also, let's face it, it *is* **really hard** to hold a pose for so many long, deep breaths.

It seems funny now, but it took a long time to get there (like, a really, really long time). The first realization came just in the smallest awareness that the busy script I kept playing in my head wasn't even true in the first place. It didn't have to be. It was of my design. Finding that it was tied to my self-worth would take even longer.

The point is, these practices that were just a part of a checklist titled, "How to Be a Really Good Person That Impresses Everyone," really did help me. They had some true merit. It didn't matter why I was doing them, what my motivation was, or who it impressed because it helped get to the layer under the layer eventually—regardless.

It turns out, there is ample scientific validation for these practices as well. Besides the countless medical studies that point to dramatic improvements in mental health due to yoga and meditation, there are just as many that show their effects on physical well-being too. Yoga and meditation have been shown in numerous studies to: decrease stress, reduce anxiety, reduce inflammation, improve heart health, increase the quality of life, relieve symptoms of depression, reduce chronic pain, improve sleep, increase lung function, and relieve migraines. I could keep going, but do I need to? This woman (me) with multiple autoimmune diseases causing prolific pain, regular migraines, lung and heart disease, who couldn't get a handle on her own stress and anxiety (while in her early thirties, I should add), needed no further proof or research. She was THE prime candidate.

There are fascinating biological explanations for their efficacy, too. These would be the next layer that would be exposed by peeling away the one just above it and continuing to follow my own curiosity and trust my growing intuition.

—

Invitation:

Have you tried meditation or any mindfulness practice—yoga, focusing on your breath, maybe an active meditation like fishing or running or surfing—anything that helps you continually train your mind to be more present and less lost in the past or in the future? Can you think of a specific moment in which you were truly present and just that presence allowed you to experience that moment so much more fully? Write about it. Now continue to plan for other ways you can support yourself in this way. Download a meditation app, go for a walk where you focus strictly on the sights and sounds immediately around you, or try a yoga class (you can find them free on YouTube). What will you do and when?

Real: Rest, Digest, Heal

"Between stimulus and response, there is a space. In that space is our power to choose our response. In our response lies our growth and our freedom." - Victor A. Frankl

One reason meditation and yoga made positive impacts on my health had to do my central nervous system. Remember learning about the nervous system in high school science class? Let me refresh your memory. Deeply rooted in the most primitive, mammalian section of our brain, we have something called the sympathetic nervous system. It's a good thing we do, because we would have been eaten by a saber-toothed tiger long ago without it. (I'm just guessing here.) The sympathetic nervous system controls our fear response in ways we cannot directly control. For instance, it's what gives us the surge of adrenaline when we see said saber-toothed tiger on our six, allows us to run as quickly as possible in the other direction or even turn, face him, stab him with that spear in our hand, and take him home to cook over the fire and feed to our family. Man: 1, Saber-toothed tiger: 0. We're still around, after all.

We can't directly control that adrenaline response. We can't say to ourselves, *Okay, brain. I need thirty ccs of adrenaline injected directly into my nervous system at this time, please.* That's a good thing too because if that were the case, that prehistoric cat would be licking his chops right now. (What is the correct dose of adrenaline anyway?) Nope. It doesn't work that way. Our sympathetic nervous system just takes over. It sends out the directions quicker than we even think about thinking about doing so.

Our sympathetic nervous system also dilates our pupils, increases our heart rate, makes us sweat, and elevates our blood pressure. We don't have to fill out any paperwork to get our bodies to do those things. There's no red tape. It just happens naturally if everything is functioning as it should. Nice, right? I'm guessing you've heard many times, this part of our nervous system is in charge of what people like to call the fight or flight response.

This isn't intended to be a science lesson, so I'll get on with it. To really understand the sympathetic nervous system, you also need to know what it can't do. The sympathetic nervous system does have limits, and common nomenclature likes to call those limits—rest, digest, and heal. That is the responsibility of the parasympathetic nervous system. Yep, there's an entirely different system in charge of all that goodness. This is also great news, because if we were always in fight or flight mode, we wouldn't be around anymore either. We would have died of heart failure long before we slayed anything in our path.

All of this means, the more we're calm (translate, slow heart rate and low blood pressure and less adrenaline) the more we're in parasympathetic mode. Conversely, the more we're stressed (translate, high heart rate and high blood pressure and increased adrenaline), the more we're in sympathetic mode.

Don't get me wrong. I like Mr. Sympathetic. He saves lives, but he's afraid all the time and he's all hopped up on adrenaline, too. If he had it his way, he'd use so much adrenaline so often that he'd cause the whole system to malfunction (ever heard of adrenal fatigue?). Let's face it. He's not good at budgeting. He'll have us running at 90mph, with the gas light on, and driving off a cliff if we let him have both hands on the wheel. We don't want him driving the car full-time.

Maybe you picked up on the fact that the part of our nervous system that allows our bodies to repair and heal is controlled by the parasympathetic nervous system. It makes sense then, that a person trying to heal in any way—physically or emotionally— may want to try shifting into parasympathetic mode more often.

In retrospect, it's clear that I was behaving in a way that put me in sympathetic mode (fight or flight) much more frequently than necessary. Obvious now, this was not a mode from which I could heal, but a mode from which I could get a quick hit of adrenaline to combat the bone-deep exhaustion I was feeling. I wasn't, after all, running from saber-toothed tigers looking for their next meal, as my ancestors were. I was trying to, for example, get two young girls out the door and in the car with matching shoes and not be late. This now required a habitual process of staying calm for as long as possible until the last moment when I'd begin threatening, guilting, and yelling enough to throw my sympathetic nervous system into gear. That would give me the adrenaline dump that would supply the energy to do what was necessary to get out the door. Then I could take a deep breath once I put the car in drive. When this deep breath allowed my parasympathetic nervous system to take over again, I reflected on my behavior, apologized, and tried to form a plan that would ensure it wouldn't happen again.

The problem was, it would continue happening until I recognized it was a self-induced scenario that gave me the energy to do the thing I was dreading each morning. Realizations like this one—there were many more to follow—were only stumbled upon out of dumb luck or what I'd like to think of more often as divine intervention. I didn't know that my body's needed to move into parasympathetic mode more often in order to heal. I just knew that this way of being I'd unconsciously come to wasn't working any longer. I needed to find a new way that allowed for more peace and less stress in my life. Quitting my job wasn't the quick fix I thought it would be, because all of the under workings and root causes that had got me to that place were still at play.

What I would come to learn, after conscious efforts to reduce my stress response to the stimuli in my life, was that my sympathetic nervous system was also being held hostage by the trauma I'd never dealt with from my preteen and teen years. My body still carried the memory of those experiences, regardless of my continued efforts to deny and repress them. The trauma was also triggered every time I received a new diagnosis, subjected myself to an invasive medical test, procedure, or surgery and was given a less than favorable prognosis. This meant that my body was much quicker to throw itself into sympathetic mode. It meant that using my sympathetic nervous system came much more naturally to my body than my parasympathetic nervous system did. I was exhausted, felt pain all over my body, had frequent headaches that made me physically ill, and literally couldn't digest my food. Like so many with chronic illness and autoimmune disease, my stomach was almost always full and bloated.

Spelled out clearly here, connecting the dots from problem to solution seems so clear. It took years to put it together. Doing so led to another revelation. Though my finger wasn't on the proverbial button of shifting into or out of fight or flight mode, there were many pieces that I could control. No, I can't tell my body when to dump some happy hormones or energetic ones or how much I needed. I can't tell my heart how many times to beat per minute to reduce or increase the pressure in my veins, but I can control my breath. Focusing on my breath does control those things.

By focusing on my breath, I can physically control which part of my brain is active. I can move from the mammalian part of my brain to my frontal lobe. There's a lot more choice there. Focusing on my breath, slowing it, also slows my heart rate. Slowing my heart rate and moving the activity in my brain guides my body through an entirely different chemical, hormonal, and internal processes.

It made sense then, that if my body and mind and soul were full of inflammation (stress, accelerated aging, pain, anxiety, depression), I needed to be in parasympathetic more often to allow healing. My parasympathetic nervous system would allow my body to begin to heal itself—exactly what it was designed to do.

—

Invitation:

Is your body spending a little too much time in fight-or-flight mode? What's your hunch? Does your body have a disproportionate reaction to the circumstances in your life? The next time you feel anxious, emotional, angry, or worried, try tuning into your body. Take some time to feel what those feelings *feel* like. That sounds repetitive, but the idea is just to notice if your chest feels tight; if your face feels hot; if your head hurts over your right eye; if your right lung feels like it's collapsed; if you feel *anything*. Become aware of how and where you experience feelings in your body without judging or trying to change or repress them. Now that you're noticing, take some very deep breaths while you allow those feelings to move through your body completely. Don't rush it. Let it take as long as it needs to. The next time you feel like your throat is constricted, for example, you can say, "When I'm angry, I usually feel like I'm choking. I must be angry." Then breathe and breathe and breathe again, letting yourself experience and name your anger. Without rushing it, let it pass fully through your body. Repeat. Repeat. Repeat—notice, name, experience, let go.

Real: Journaling

"If you haven't healed it, every time you think about a negative event from your past, your body produces the exact same chemicals in the body as when it happened. That means you relive the experience hundreds of times simply because you haven't let it go." - changeofair.com

One night after enjoying a couple of orange juices spiked with vodka—my typical defenses being dulled; some extra time and energy on my hands sans a nine-to-five plus and a few tools in my belt after trying so many tricks to get better—a lifelong friend called my bluff when I mindlessly mentioned starting a blog together. This possibility incited much fear and many more reasons to give old sympathetic a go with self-induced deadlines and to-do lists, but it did another thing, too; it gave me the chance to write about what was I was going through, trying out, questioning, and wondering about. I was able to post into the vast inter-workings of the Internet, words that the severe introvert in me couldn't, at that point, say aloud or bring up in conversation.

Much of what I wrote at first was superficial, like how to read ingredients to choose the best peanut butter or reworking a childhood recipe to make it "healthy" while still being comforting. Sometimes though, I'd let my defenses down enough to quickly push publish on stories about that monumental visit to the chiropractor or writing and saying affirmations.

After a while, a realization sank in—this writing was much more beneficial to me than to our few dozen readers, largely family and friends. The more I wrote about what was important to me and what I was going through and learning beyond the surface, the better I felt inside and the more equipped I was to handle the ups and downs of life around me. This writing was another healing practice.

It wasn't a quick fix like I was so long on the hunt for, but little by little, it helped expose and peel away the next layer and the next layer after that. Through which I was able to reestablish a connection with a dear friend.

Since then, through reading and my own trial and error, I've come to understand just how healing the act of writing is. Studies show simple journaling, without an audience or reader, to be *just as effective* (sometimes more) as seeing a counselor or therapist. Further, they've found that it not only helps with mental and emotional health, as might be expected, but writing about thoughts, feelings, and experiences has positive physical benefits in patients with cancer and other chronic illnesses, like lung, heart, and autoimmune disease. Journaling has even been shown to make physical wounds heal faster.

It is my nature and my go-to defense to be skeptical of these types of interventions and treatments. In retrospect, I recognize this skepticism as resistance to doing the more difficult work of healing that I'd long avoided. I found changing my diet and exercising to exhaustion much easier. My skeptic's heart and reluctance needed some real evidence to push past this resistance and answer what I continued to be led toward.

I found some evidence to legitimize where I was already being led in the book *Expressive Writing: Words that Heal* by James Pennebaker. In it, he lists several studies that tout the various benefits of expressive writing—writing about emotional, stressful, and/or traumatic life experiences.

It was in his book that I first learned about the Adverse Childhood Experiences Study (Kaiser Permanete, 1995-1997), a study of over 9,508 people that found trauma in childhood to be a strong predictor of serious adult illness. Participants filling out a questionnaire studied seven categories of adverse childhood experiences, including psychological, physical, or sexual abuse; violence against mother; or living with household members who were substance abusers, mentally ill or suicidal, or ever imprisoned. The findings showed a relationship between the number of adverse childhood experiences and an increase in both behaviors considered health risks (drug use, alcoholism, depression, etc.), smoking, poor self-rated health, number of sexual partners, STDs, increased physical inactivity, and obesity. The study also found a relationship between the number of adverse childhood experiences and the presence of adult diseases, including heart disease, lung disease, cancer, and even skeletal fractures. In short, the study found a strong relationship between the extent of subjection to abuse or household dysfunction during childhood and multiple risk factors for several of the leading causes of death in adults.

Pennebaker then sites something further, when he details his own research. He found that having a traumatic experience was certainly bad for people in many ways, but people who experienced trauma and kept that trauma a secret experienced worse effects. Not talking to others about trauma, he learned, placed people at even higher risk for major and minor illness compared to people who did talk about their traumas. His research also found that adults experiencing major trauma before the age of seventeen visited the doctor for illness twice as often as those who hadn't experienced trauma. Of those who experienced trauma, the adults who kept it a secret went to the doctor forty percent more than those who chose to talk about the trauma.

There are many other studies to back up these findings and the benefits of expressive writing and journaling, but this was my first peek at any sort of documentation that pointed to a direct link in covering-up, denying, and excusing away what I'd been through as I was growing up and the physical disorders I experienced as an adult. It validated my own hunch—the body and mind are magical and powerful and mystical, connected in a way that we can't see but that can provide great benefit or detriment to our health, depending on our choice of direction.

Many spiritual experts have weighed in on the damage of holding old narratives, pain, and trauma within us. Eckhart Tolle calls this the pain body—the weight of unresolved suffering from our childhood that we carry with us as adults that perpetuates painful (sometimes generational) narratives in our present. He says:

> "Every addiction arises from an unconscious refusal to face and move through your own pain. Every addiction starts with pain and ends with pain. Whatever the substance you are addicted to—alcohol, food, legal or illegal drugs, or a person—you are using something or somebody to cover up your pain."

The first step in releasing yourself from the unconscious effects of this pain body, in his words, is to,

> "...observe it, feel its energy field within you, and take your attention into it, the identification is broken. A higher dimension of consciousness has come in. I call it presence. You are now the witness or the watcher of the pain-body. This means that it cannot use you anymore by pretending to be you, and it can no longer replenish itself through you. You have found your own innermost strength." (The Power of Now)

Michael A. Singer also discusses stored negative experiences and thoughts at length in his book, *The Untethered Soul: The Journey Beyond Yourself*. He describes it as held energy that creates blocks in your life, referring to it as Samskara—the term for leftover mental impressions of thoughts, actions, and intentions in the yogic tradition. He writes about letting them go in his book. Saying that by holding onto them, "You're locking your illness inside yourself and it will only get worse...Just keep letting them go."

Expressive writing and journaling were a way to help me release the past pain and trauma that I'd carried for years, locked away deep inside. As I allowed myself the freedom and space to follow my curiosities, I found that there are other ways of moving beyond the uncontrollable sympathetic response of our nervous system, the knee jerk reactions from a lifetime of unconscious habit and the genetic predisposition of our ancestors' adaptations for survival.

Meditation, yoga, and journaling proved to be very beneficial in all of the above. While they could be done in the moment if needed or in case of an emotional overload emergency, more often they required developing a routine and practice. I set aside time each day to ensure they were prioritized and that they actually happened. There were other, more spontaneous, practices that I worked into my day on an as-needed basis. They could be done from almost anywhere at any time when I felt myself being pulled into stress mode.

Dancing and singing were one way. The song choice was key here—picking a song that elevated my mood and energy level rather than reinforced whatever depths I might have felt myself being drawn into. Some people call this raising your energetic vibration. Another way I learned to shift into a place of consciousness, raise my vibration if you will, or move out of fight or flight, was to spend some time with animals. My dog and my chickens have a way of lifting me into the present moment, grounding me in what is important, and finding gratitude for the simplest things. I began to lean into this feeling and lean on the animals that were dear to me when I needed a shift.

Once these practices allowed me to separate myself from my thoughts, ideas, and incessant internal dialog, I could: notice them without judgment; choose not to attach to them; let them figuratively float by; use affirmations to write new stories; live more fully in the present by not attaching to my monkey mind; find gratitude for all the good in my life, and enjoy more love and deeper connection through being open and present. These are practices I continue to work through today. I imagine they will require a lifetime of intentionality. I'm okay with that. I no longer see them as a box to be checked off a to-do list, but a means through which I'm able to gain the clarity and understanding to create and live the life I desire—fulfill the purpose of my soul's presence here on earth.

—

Invitation:

Consider how a journaling practice might aid in your healing and growth. Think about a cozy space in your home where you would feel relaxed, open, and comfortable enough to write about yourself. What would your ideal journal look like? What type of notebook could you gift yourself to communicate your commitment to becoming what your soul is calling you to—your authentic self? Think of the size, color, and texture of the book you'd use to prioritize sitting down to write in each day. What will it feel like to do so? Make it happen! Need a little help with what to journal about? Here's what I do:

I don't journal every day, but my goal is to journal at least four times per week. That seems to be the minimum amount to keep my head clear and above water. Journaling happens in the morning, with my first cup of tea and right after I meditate and pray. This gives me the best chance of being present and intentional throughout the day. It sets me up for the best day possible. My daily journaling includes:

- Gratitude: I list three to five things I'm grateful for and specify why.
- Self-love: I write at least one thing about my body or myself that I appreciate.
- Desired feelings: From Danielle LaPorte's *Desire Map* course, I learned to focus on how I want to feel for the day, rather than what I need/want to get done. I remind myself of these feelings every day. Then I write what actions, thoughts, and beliefs will allow me to feel the way I'd like.
- Affirmations: Learning to retrain unconscious thought processes and beliefs I've held about myself for decades is not a simple process. First, there is the noticing, without judgment or disapproval. Noticing

sounds like, *Oh, there you are. I hear you. I see what you're doing.* Next, there's rewriting the script. Affirmations are one way to do this. Countless examples and abundant information about affirmations can be found from a quick Internet search. I won't belabor them here. I'll just say that affirmations work best for me when I write them as though I'm looking down from my highest self. I try to imagine what stories I want to be done with or where I desire to be at a given point in the future. For example, a year from now, do I still want to hear myself saying what a terrible mother I am? Of course not. In that case, I might write an affirmation that's something like, *I am a living example of the empowered, authentic, and beautiful human I want my daughters to grow into*, or, *I love myself so fully and completely that my love spills over, enveloping my daughters, and causing them to do the same.* This process naturally makes space to observe where I'm at now, imagine where I want to go, then talk to myself as though I'm already there.

I've repeated the old narratives to myself so many times that I can't expect to write an affirmation once and be done with it. When things get tough or I get low, that mean voice will creep in again. That's why I've had to write and say (doing both is most effective in changing the script) the same affirmation for months, maybe years, sometimes. I write it and say it, morning after morning, over and over again, until I don't need to anymore, until my self-talk or my actions have changed or I've reached whatever milestone my affirmation has guided me toward. Then I write a new one, and so it goes, again and again. I like to work with several at a time, but no more than eight—too many at once makes them forgetful, in my opinion.

- Inspiration: I write a quote, lyric, thought, or idea I find inspiring. I find inspiration in podcasts, books (for some this might mean a daily Bible verse), music, people in my life, and even social media. I find inspiration anywhere, everywhere. Writing it down daily has me constantly on the look-out. It also means that when I do scroll on social media, most often I'm looking for something inspiring I can take with me as fuel for my day rather than using it to repeat negative thought patterns and feelings. Inspiration's never a bad thing.
- Anything else that doesn't fit in any of the above: Ideas, thoughts,

synthesizing information, what I might be having trouble moving past, areas I might need help, etc.

While this daily journaling practice helps my mental health dramatically, it is not the same as expressive writing/journaling—about twenty minutes of sustained, free-form style writing about past experiences and traumas that continue to raise issues, for several concurrent days. You can read much more about that process in the book I mentioned in this chapter. If you're recovering from trauma, it can be done before or in conjunction with the practice I outlined above. I am not a mental health professional, and none of my experience is intended as medical advice. Walking through trauma, depression, and physical health issues are complicated and individual processes. Opening up old wounds should not be done alone. Please ask for the help of your doctor and/or mental health professional.

Real: Prescriptions

"Before you heal someone, ask him if he's willing to give up the things that made him sick." - Hippocrates

I had a rheumatologist, a pulmonologist, and now found myself in a sterile room waiting for a cardiologist. This specialist was added to the list after the echo-cardiogram showing pulmonary hypertension. There was a quiet knock, knock briefly before he entered the room. This was nothing new. His quick speech and hurried manner were nothing new, either. The majority of doctor's appointments went this way—too many patients, too little time.

What was different was the content of what he was saying. After he asked many questions while glancing at my chart on his computer screen, he took out a piece of paper and began writing on it like it was a prescription pad. I never had a prescription written like this one. He spoke about diet and research, something new also. Specifically, he talked about all the evidence supporting a vegan diet to reverse heart disease. In the end, his prescription was a list of just four items:

1. Nutrition
2. Exercise
3. Love and Connection
4. Mental Health

As he wrote the last one he explained, "By mental health, I don't just mean meditate or do yoga." I shook my head repeatedly, in agreement maybe, but more out of shock for what I was hearing. "I mean you need to pick up the rug and sweep everything out beneath it. Deal with anything you may not have yet."

"*Okay,*" my only response. He didn't leave much room for discussion. I would leave his office with homework—the list of four prescriptions above accompanied by a list of food documentaries about a plant-based diet. I had a couple of weeks to try everything out until I saw him again, after a long list of subsequent tests were completed.

My expectation going into the cardiologist's office that day was that it would be up to me to remain positive and hopeful in the wake of some bleak news. In reality, I left with hope and enthusiasm for what was to come and the part I had to play in that. The doctor's words, though rehearsed and rushed, affirmed all the work I had already done—the less conventional, typically not doctor recommended methods. When I asked my other specialists about diet or exercise or anything other than prescriptions I might be able to control, I most often heard, "You can try it, but it probably won't do anything." I expected to hear the same again. For the first time, someone with doctoral specialty initials after their name was not only saying, "Yeah! Do that!" He was saying, "Do more than that. There's research to prove it can help more than any pill I could prescribe."

There were no guarantees, no certainties about the length of life left in my heart and lungs and body. But there was plenty of possibility. I had work to do. The ball was in my court, and I was ready and willing.

—

Invitation:

Look at the four prescriptions above. Which of the four items in the list is your body, mind, and soul in need of most? Is it what you're putting in your body? Is it how you're moving (or not) your body? Are you in need of more love and connection? Do you need to pick up that rug and sweep all the dust bunnies out from underneath it? Remember, my cardiologist "prescribed" these four items to me, because they are the most widely, research-based methods to improve health, including heart and lung disease. Pick one, the one your intuition is telling you is most important to you at this time. There's a large possibility that one happens to be the one you'd like to work on *least* of all. What is one thing you can begin doing today (or tomorrow) and the days after that to improve in that area? Hint: maybe the one thing is learning more about it, but *eventually*, when you've learned enough, you need to take action.

Real: Connection

"People who feel loved live longer; have fewer colds, lower blood pressure, and lower cancer rates; and have fewer heart attacks." - Deepak Chopra

Humans are wired for connection. Being a part of and connected with a tribe was imperative to historical human survival. Perhaps that's why the research on the health benefits of connection are so staggering.

One well-known study found that lack of social connection is a greater detriment to health than obesity, smoking, and high blood pressure, combined. Moreover, having strong social connections increases lifespan by fifty percent, positively affects immune function, and allows quicker recovery from illness. Connection also lowers anxiety and depression while increasing self-esteem and empathy. This means connection creates a cycle that allows for even more connection by growing traits that foster trust and cooperation with others.

If I was truly serious about improving my health for my daughters' sake, our family's sake, for my own, I would have to get rid of the tired excuses and hang-ups I had that justified my isolation and loneliness. I could no longer use the excuse of being an introvert or stubbornly try to do everything for myself or shut down in difficult social moments. True connection required deliberate action in walking toward what I previously found comfort in walking away from. It meant saying yes more to invitations and opening up more when I would have previously been afraid or reluctant to speak.

Life called my bluff, and it was time for me to step out of my comfort zone. This took intentional action on my part. I wrote affirmations like:

I speak of myself freely and easily.

And

I'm not afraid to share my truth.

I wrote goals that involved seeking and nurturing authentic connections to women in my life, something I'd previously done a poor job of. It was important for me to be deliberate about those I sought connections with. The basis of these relationships needed to be founded in qualities other than my people-pleasing and perfectionism. They had to be with women who maintained healthy boundaries and respected and nurtured mine. This meant moving away from some past relationships and growing new ones. To do this, required seeking new opportunities to meet like-minded men and women that also challenged me to grow and learn.

I created an investor group, including men and women, in hopes of meeting regularly to learn and inspire one another. That failed. I carried on anyway. I reached out to women who inspired me through blogs and social media and did my best to grow relationships with those who reached out to me. I attended conferences and meet-ups related to areas in which I wanted to grow and learn. I went out of my way, always uncomfortably, to make connections with those I felt naturally drawn to. I joined groups, invited people over, accepted more invitations, and genuinely made an effort to stay open and willing to connect in a healthy way to others. Not everyone or every attempt was a match, but I knew better each time which connections were bringing me growth and freedom and which were repeating the old relationship patterns I was trying to break.

Connecting more meant continuing to open up to my husband and daughters. I worked at improving my ability to know and understand myself, my needs, and my desires, so that I could communicate those with my family. I began telling stories about my past in an effort to let them "see" all of me, and I started to open up when I felt like shutting down. With practice, all of these actions got easier, but I continue to be a work in progress in this area too. I simply take small, imperfect steps in the moments that present themselves, and deliberately seek connection rather than avoiding it.

—

Invitation:

Where have you been holding back—closing yourself off, putting up walls, or saying no to invitations to connect? What would happen if you said yes; you opened up; you got real; you let your true, authentic, core-self show and shine? What is your fear? Write that down. Now, what if that fear came true? Would you be okay? I thought so. Getting real with people just lets us find our people, right? If we show our true selves, chances are it will deepen the connections we already have or are trying to forge. If it doesn't, we simply have a clearer picture of what we need to walk away from. This allows us to walk toward what is truly meant for us. What will you say yes to? How will you let your light shine?

Real: Love

"Find the love you seek, by first finding the love within yourself. Learn to rest in that place within you. That is your true home." - Sri Ravi Shankar

Connections formed as I began to open myself up, to be gentler and kinder with myself in my vulnerability. I allowed myself to do and say things I previously kept close to my chest, fearing what others might think of my thoughts, words, and actions. I trusted myself and others with my true, authentic self—stepping gingerly in this direction with the awareness that I wouldn't always get it right. I knew I would make mistakes in learning this new way of being, that the me I was presenting to the world now would not always be pretty or perfect, but it would be real. I didn't entirely know what *real* was yet, but I was willing to move forward and allow myself grace in the process of finding it.

One of the first moments that put this choice to the test was being a guest on a podcast with my husband. We talked about finding financial freedom through real estate with a family in tow. This involved pitching ourselves, communicating openly during the podcast, and then sharing this with friends and family that we hadn't shared so openly with before, all of which required deep vulnerability.

I've never had a problem with lying. It is well illustrated that I've had plenty of problems, but lying was not one of those. The majority of my life has been spent shielding and hiding. Opening up, being authentic, being real was difficult for me not because I had a habit of lying, but because I had a habit of only trusting myself with my thoughts and past and emotions. I locked them in tight, kept them to myself, and caused my own loneliness in separation by denying my trust to even those closest to me. I didn't know how to tell people what I wanted, liked, or was important to me. Years of practice at not talking about myself meant I barely knew the answers to those things either. I'm adept at deflecting by asking others about themselves.

This allowed me to develop a deep empathy and interest in others, making them feel truly seen and heard. This is a superpower, but a superpower used without a full knowledge and complete understanding of the gift can become a curse. I was so full of, so invested in, the needs, desires, likes, hopes, and dreams of others, that there was no room left for mine. Empathy can be overwhelming, all-consuming, when the empath attaches to all that they feel in others. It became increasingly difficult to separate myself and my emotions from the emotions and desires of others. I didn't know where they ended and I began. I knew so much about everyone else, even more than they could communicate to me with words, but I knew very little about myself. Often, the simplest of questions from my husband in an attempt to know me better, to listen to me, would end in a full-on cry fest. I couldn't talk about myself without crying. I still have trouble occasionally. I've continued to talk about and explore my emotions through tears and ask myself questions. I didn't like sobbing while telling my husband what I wanted, what I was afraid of, or the barrage of negative self-talk I finally heard coming from within me. I did it anyway, encouraged by his insistence and patience.

That's why this idea of sharing so much on a podcast was such a big step. Before beginning the recording of the episode, I took a deep breath, said a prayer, and gave myself permission to not be perfect at it. Then when I watched the YouTube version after it was released, I did the same. For the first time I could remember, I felt proud of the woman I saw and heard in that video. Sure, I was attracted to all the imperfections at first. That was my habit. I zeroed in on a phrase I repeated too much or the way my arms or my teeth looked. Then I reminded myself of my intention, and I watched it as though I was someone else. I saw the woman in that video like she was the little girl from so long ago in the wild, in the city, all alone. I saw the truth. She was beautiful and brave and generous in her transformation and her openness to share authentically and vulnerably. I saw through the outside to the intention inside—to inspire and help others. I was proud of her. I was proud of myself. That was a big step.

I believe it was only because of that authentic vulnerability that the mystical powers of connection began to happen. As I opened up and began to shed all that I thought had been protecting me through the years, all the unconscious coping skills, I cleared space for more authenticity within. Some of that space allowed me to give myself time and energy to ask and answer the questions I'd been avoiding for so long. What did I need? What did I want? What was important to me? What was my purpose now? It also made space for people to come into my life, people that aligned with my purpose and people that helped me find and take the next steps necessary to get there.

One of those connections happened through social media. A woman that heard the podcast, reached out to me. She let me know she related to our story, how it inspired her, and that she was grateful. I had prayed for this connection. Then I took it a step further and made it a theme for my year—to seek and create connections whenever possible. An authentic, two-way connection was hard for me, so I needed to make it a clear focus if I was to get better at it. The cardiologist prescribed it, right? That's why I took this light, brief message on Instagram so seriously. I didn't brush it off. I was grateful for it. It felt like a gift, and I treated it like one, trying to keep the conversation going.

Then one day, a day that I felt like I could use a friend, my new Instagram buddy just happened to reach out to me. It didn't feel like a coincidence. She told me that she just received her Feng Shui certification, and she wondered if I'd be willing to help her practice it. I'm guessing this was a message she sent to many people online as a step in creating and building her business. I understood that as my stomach took a dive and my feet wanted to run as far away from Feng Shui as possible. I also felt nudged to step toward those things that were making me uncomfortable, like getting to know myself and finding authentic connections with others. So I stepped closer, thinking *I* could help *her*, as she'd asked, and leaned into connecting even though it felt uncomfortable. What I didn't know, what I couldn't see coming, is the way *she* was helping *me*.

She needed to know what "blocks" I was having trouble with-in my life. Being so new to this mystical, magical world, I needed a lot of clarification with the term blocks. Asking a lot of questions about this word bought time to create a lot of resistance around becoming even more vulnerable with someone on the Internet. I mean, was I really going to message someone through Instagram about things I was having trouble moving past or accomplishing in my life? I was just beginning to be honest with myself about these things and could barely utter them to my husband.

After some soul searching, I told her that, though I had quit my job to allow myself more time and less stress, I'd continually sought and created new jobs for myself since. One of my blocks was finding more work and more ways to create income after seemingly putting that behind me. What I didn't explicitly tell her was that in the few years since leaving teaching, I had:

1. Babysat an infant
2. Sold essential oils
3. Sold skincare products
4. Began homeschooling both of my children
5. Co-created a blog
6. Created a real estate investment company with my husband (that now had 19 rental homes)
7. Began freelance writing
8. Got a license and began selling crop insurance

There was also this recurring issue of my health. I'd been doing so much to cultivate health within my body, yet I kept hearing about new issues that needed addressing from my doctors. Was it a coincidence that the summer she reached out to me I had been told that I had yet another new condition?

Not long before I heard from her, I'd had a right heart catheterization to find definitive answers about the pulmonary hypertension diagnosis. This was essentially a heart surgery, minor surgery, but heart surgery nonetheless. Google told me that the consequences of this diagnosis were nothing to balk at—requiring far more money and time in medical treatments and shortening my life expectancy (three to five years) much more than any of my other autoimmune-related conditions to this point. I couldn't shake the nagging feeling of responsibility that I'd somehow continued to invite and allow doctors, medical tests, and diagnoses into my life subconsciously though I felt in my heart I didn't want any of it. Why did medical issues keep coming up?

From an outside view, perhaps, I was a stay-at-home mom with an abundance of time and freedom on her hands, but on the inside, I was still constantly trying to prove my worth to myself and to others by hustling. So many things become obvious when we say them aloud or write them down because someone is kind enough to ask and show sincere interest. The internal struggle that was leading to the persistent, outward issues seems so clear in hindsight and when typed on a page. Yet at the moment, I was truly wondering, *Why do I keep creating work for myself? and Why do I continue to need to be "fixed" medically? Am I broken?*

The gift I was given from the kindness of, for all intents and purposes, a stranger over the Internet was a gentle nudge in the direction of finding, cultivating, and growing love and acceptance for myself. That's right—self-love through Feng Shui. I can use the word friend in reference to this stranger because there is no better word for someone who would reach through a screen with the purest of intentions, show sincere interest in another, and help that person develop a love and respect for themselves.

When she read what I had to tell her about my blocks, she replied,

"It seems that the unworthy feeling and the autoimmune disease are related. Perhaps the unworthy feeling is part of the root of why your body keeps attacking itself." Then after sending her pictures of my home and the rooms within it, she asked me to tell her how I felt emotionally in certain spaces. No surprise, I couldn't answer that question easily. I didn't ask myself how I *felt* in my bedroom or living room. I didn't know the answer. It took me a long time to get back to her, but because I knew she was waiting for an answer from me, I sought an answer to her question. I asked myself how I felt. I sat in each of the rooms she requested and asked myself how they made me feel. Something that I was adept at sensing in others dumbfounded me when it came to myself.

When I finally let her know that my bedroom felt dark, she came back with, "You seem full of vibrancy and life, and your bedroom is not a reflection of that. You want to feel cozy but also like you want to fall in love in that room. (Ahem, fall in love with yourself.)" Fall in love with myself!? To do this, I was required to remove anything that did not make me feel good, add things that represented loving myself and my partner, like things in pairs, and if I could handle it, try adding some pink or red.

Outwardly these were simple tasks involving colors and furniture, pillows and lamps, but these suggestions revealed a deeper issue I had been avoiding. My difficulty in answering and acting on such seemingly simple and shallow suggestions held a mirror to some deeper workings within me. Self-love was still out of reach, but the curiosity within me told me it was necessary. I may not have been able to trust myself enough with examining the child within me that I was trying to protect through denial all these years, but curiosity was leading me there slowly. If I could learn to trust myself with room color and a couple of pillows, maybe I could begin to trust myself with more. Maybe this Feng Shui thing wasn't all about decorating. Maybe it wasn't so shallow after all.

It turned out that what would come from it was anything but shallow. Learning to trust myself with little things and giving myself the respect, time, and energy required to make these small changes in my home, required making bigger changes in the home of my soul. I had to devote time and energy to myself in the name of self-discovery. I had to value myself enough to spend money and time on things that *I* wanted but quite possibly no one else in my house would benefit from. The emotional difficulty I had with these simple tasks revealed far deeper truths. Out of self-preservation, I developed skills that allowed me to survive difficult trauma at key stages in my development as a child and young adult. These were passed on to me by the words and actions of the most significant adult relationships in my life—my mom and dad. They were self-taught, through assumptions and misgivings in the absence of guidance and presence of those adults in my life. The actions of my parents and the coping skills I had developed when they left me, taught me that my survival meant I needed to depend on others as little as possible and ensure that the people I wanted to keep around would stay. I kept them near, by making them happy. These same skills that got me this far—helped create a life that was safe, comfortable, and from outside perspectives remarkably successful—were literally killing me now. It became clear that my most radical act of healing would require loving myself as much as I loved those around me.

So, did my parents tell me that I wasn't important, I didn't matter, they didn't love me, I didn't deserve love? No. That never happened. I told myself that subconsciously every time I saw that buying beer was more important than buying food or clothes for me. On the surface, I never doubted that they loved me. They told me so. Inside though, every time they chose the step-parent that was abusive or neglectful or mentally ill over my health and well-being, I learned that my health and well-being were not what was important. I learned, from those adults and from my eleven-year-old self in their absence, that to survive I needed to shrink myself. I needed to become small and quiet, to take up little space and need even less. I learned to feel good by making other people feel better. My worth, then, was dependent on how I made other people feel, how "good" I was, how many "good" things I could do, how hard I could work, how little I required, and how perfect I could be. If I could be and do all of those things, on the outside at least, I had learned, then I wouldn't need anyone else and the people I wanted in my life would stick around. They would need me more than I needed them.

In the strangest and what can only be described as the most magical of ways, it took a stranger on the Internet and the art of Feng Shui to point this out to me.

Logic and rationality had little to do with my steps forward. Those things had gotten me to the place I was searching for a way out of. I didn't cry out to God out of logic and rationality. I went to prayer from a place of mysticism, searching for a magical response to my pleas. I humbled myself when those answers came to me in mystical and magical ways and chose to step forward and act on them in trust.

What I know now is, God is not concerned with efficiency. The Universe does not work through finding the quickest way from point A to point B. Source does not deal in those things. It took years for me to finally make the connection that my body kept breaking (in part at least) because I was acting in a way that told it that I was broken—that I was not worthy. I did not get that message overnight or the first time it was sent to me. I was given the message over and over again. It finally started to sink in, in the tiniest way, one bit at a time.

Before I could love others in a healthy way, I had to love myself. Before I could love myself, I had to find an unconditional worthiness of that love within. Those were the steps:

1. Worthiness
2. Self-Love
3. Healthy, Loving Relationships

That was the new order. I had literally been going about it in the opposite order my whole life, never understanding where all of the dis-ease was coming from.

—

Invitation:

Remember a few chapters ago when you started working on forgiving yourself—when you took deep breaths in and breathed out letting go? Then you did it again and again and again and again. Probably, you're still doing it. Good! Have you started to notice a space? Maybe you've started to feel a little lighter, as you've let go of the weight you've been carrying. Or perhaps, you feel an openness after releasing things that you weren't meant to hold onto. That space is inviting you to fill it up with something new. Let's fill it up with love, okay? Put your kindest, gentlest, most appreciative thoughts—the ones you have for yourself, your body, for how far you've come, for your very being—put all of those things in that open space. Carry those things around with you now. I bet they won't be so heavy. I bet they'll feel like light.

Real: It's All In Your Head

"The wound is where the light enters." - Rumi

Learning to manage and control the pain and inflammation in my body due to autoimmune disease turned out to be something I just couldn't hack my way through. There was no quick fix, no "one-and-done". In fact, I quit trying to hack my life entirely. That's the best way I've found to truly *live* it.

Learning to heal my body began with a handful of pills several times a day, which thankfully, led to the search for a much less pharmaceutical and much more holistic, natural approach. There are so many lifestyle choices I can control, that require no prescription pad at all—food, exercise, stress reduction, love and connection, and acknowledgment and awareness.

I used to think that my rheumatologist was placating me when she'd say things like, "Watch your stress," or "Routine is so important." I thought it meant my illness wasn't real because it was in my mind. Now

I know it's very real and it's very much in my mind, too. It's all connected. Trying to heal one without the other proved time and time again not to work. I did need prescriptions, after all, to suppress my immune system so that it would quit attacking my lungs and nose and ears and other healthy tissue and organs. Just as important, I needed to work at peeling back all the layers of self-protection I'd surrounded myself in throughout the years. I needed to get to the core of what I'd been ignoring for so long. All of the above continue to be necessary for my own, true healing—body, mind, and soul. I'm grateful for it all.

I have a routine now, one that helps me maintain and improve my health in all the ways. It calms my nervous system, keeps me open and grounded, and nourishes my body and mind, fueling it for whatever steps may be next. This routine includes daily:

- Meditation
- Reading
- Journaling - gratitude, affirmations, goals, how I want to feel and the actions that will get me to those feelings
- Movement/Exercise
- Rituals - drinking tea
- Eating whole foods (fruits and vegetables) that make me feel good - avoiding sugars, most grains, and processed foods

It's not *all* in my head, it's in my body, too. They are connected. Where one goes, the other follows. I'm grateful for tools that continue to improve the health of both. There was no hacking, just loving myself enough to make the time and space to take care of myself and bring awareness where it wasn't before. It's just love, awareness, and then release from here on out—love, awareness, release; love, awareness, release; love, awareness, release—and I release, and I release, over and over again.

—

Invitation:

Here's your chance. Write down everything you love about yourself, all the best stuff. Write about everything you want to love about yourself as though you already do. Now, breathe in all that love. All of it. Deeply. On your out-breath, release anything that is not love. All of it. Breath in love. Breath out anything that's not love, anything you need to release. In: love. Out: not love…and release, and release, and release, over and over again.

Real: Going Home

"I decided to make a home for myself, inside myself. In the dirty, cracked mess of me. I decided to love it all." - Laura McKowen, We Are the Luckiest

This last Christmas was not much different from the many before it. I once again released that long exhale at the close of last year and the beginning of this one, letting out a sigh that I'd been holding for far too long. I know that I'm not alone feeling the weight of Christmas, in saying the Holidays are hard for me. I can see it on the strained faces of friends and family as we go in for heartfelt hugs and hear it in their words of agreement when I'm vulnerable enough to admit it aloud to them.

Christmas celebrations remind me of the painful childhood memories I carried with me for far too long. The angry separation and subsequent divorce, alcoholic step-dads, and crashing in the basements of high-school friends—everything that made me feel like I didn't belong. Instead of voicing the shame that I carried with me as a result, I hid it away inside. I told no one, but I never really felt like I had a place of my own, a place to call home.

For all of these reasons, I worked hard to create a real home for my own children. I've also worked hard to let go of the unhealthy beliefs and coping mechanisms of those years of my life. Yet, every year as Christmas approaches, I begin to feel the weight and dread of that old, familiar feeling—that I don't have a place to go home to. I am surrounded by family and friends that love and care for me, people that would do anything I asked or needed of them. I'm so grateful for that. And still, there won't ever be a doorknob from my childhood that I can turn saying, "I'm home!" There is not some weird room in some creepy basement somewhere with teen heartthrob pictures still on the walls waiting for me, where the light is always on and the door's always open.

I know I'm not the only one. At holiday celebrations in rooms full of people and busy chatter, I look around the room and identify it in others that feel more alone than connected, amongst so many people.

I built layers around myself out of a false sense of protection, mistakenly believing that if I depended only on me, I would avoid being hurt and rejected further. There have been so many lessons along the way to true healing, all the kinds of healing and growth—physical and emotional. I'm still learning them all. I may never master them, but I'm getting lots of practice with learning where home truly is. Home has never been about fitting in. Sometimes belonging gets mislabeled that way. Trying to "fit in" meant that I built much of my adult life around doing and being what I thought society told me I should be, what I *thought* other people wanted and needed from me, without trusting anyone enough to see the real me, not even myself. Being diagnosed with multiple chronic illnesses then climbing my way out of a darkness I was surprised to find myself in, forced me to ask questions I may not have otherwise. Being confronted with my own mortality made me dig deep and do some hard work on myself, ultimately taking many actions that were outside the norm. I started going against the flow. Asking what I needed, who I was, and ultimately, what I wanted. The answers to these questions may have made me a little weird. I didn't necessarily fit-in anywhere anymore—no street or neighborhood or town or with any social class or group or occupation. It sounds lonely. It was lonely *until* I learned arguably my most valuable lesson of all about belonging. This last Christmas reminded me of Brené Brown's words:

> "Belonging so fully to yourself that you're willing to stand alone is a wilderness—an untamed, unpredictable place of solitude and searching. It is a place as dangerous as it is breathtaking, a place as sought after as it is feared. The wilderness can often feel unholy because we can't control it, or what people think about our choice of whether to venture into the vastness or not. But it turns out to be the place of true belonging, and it's the bravest and most sacred place you will ever stand."

There are many roads to freedom but eventually they all lead to just one destination. Searching for freedom takes us all to the same place in the end. True belonging, true freedom, *home*—we carry that with us everywhere we go. It's everywhere and nowhere at once. It's within.

I belong to myself now. I go home to me.

"You are only free when you realize you belong no place—you belong every place—no place at all. The price is high. The reward is great." - Maya Angelou

Conclusion

"The most beautiful experience we can have is the mysterious—the fundamental emotion which stands at the cradle of true art and true science." - Albert Einstein

My dad and I had a lot of time for conversation on a recent week-long trip through Arizona. We were working together, growing his most recent venture as a serial entrepreneur, like his father before him. This work would take us just as far and deep into the wild as the one of my earliest memories. We spent the week driving over expansive ranches—acres and acres of dry, dusty soil far from any civilization—on B.L.M. (Bureau of Land Management) land throughout the scrubby terrain most would call desert.

We had turned off of a paved road, heading nearly straight up a steeply grated high-desert mountain path near Prescott, when I noticed the dinging. I looked over to see the gas light clearly blinking in front of him. Just minutes before, he told me that the road would go on for about twenty miles to the summit of the ranch, then another twenty or so down and back into town. Over forty miles on an empty tank, half of which being a gas-guzzling climb seemed like a stretch, even to me. Now forty-years old, this was no surprise, I had been through many similar occasions with my dad and his dad, Otto Joe. Father like son, tanks on empty were merely a challenge. I ignored the anxiety bubbling within and let my dad keep talking. This rare and real conversation felt too important to interrupt.

A desire for accuracy in telling my story had me using the long hours in the pick-up to fact check some of my memories. He was answering questions about his time in college when I was four and my brother was seven. I wanted to know about his jobs while he was in school, why he switched schools from Greeley, CO to Canyon, TX, and if my memory was correct in believing he petitioned the Dean to be able to take more than twenty-one credits (the maximum allowable for undergrads) in a single semester. The answer to the last question was yes, which also answered the second. When the first university wouldn't allow him to take as many credits as he wanted, he transferred to one that would comply with his desire to get his accounting degree in far less time than average. I was surprised to hear him describe that time as such a miserable one for him. His guilt led him to apologize again. This time for not being present much in those days. He always felt guilty about something. The older I became, the more frequent the apologies came as well. I told him those were some of the best memories of my childhood. Now he was surprised, too.

Through the years, after my first step-mom kicked me out, there would be separations and reconciliations between the two of them. There would be a move to Phoenix, Arizona and a final return of my dad alone, when their divorce was final, to help my uncle and granddad with the ranch and other businesses after my granddad's heart attack. I would slowly let Dad back into my life, and even more slowly extend trust to him, after snatching all the trust I had in him away when I was thirteen. Mostly, I stayed nights with my grandparents, where he could come over to visit me or pick me up so we could go somewhere together. Over time, I transitioned back to staying nights with him and his new wife (they remain married to this day) and going over to my grandparents' for visits during the day when I was in town and trust was restored.

Now, twenty years later and almost out of gas, our conversation had turned to addiction. He was wondering aloud if it was possible to be addicted to something other than drugs or alcohol, something like working and achieving and earning. I affirmed his musings by explaining my recent discoveries of being addicted to people-pleasing and perfecting myself, rather than his own workaholic nature.

"I think most of us adults numb and hide ourselves behind some addiction. Some of us are just lucky enough to have addictions that are socially acceptable or that people appreciate," I said.

"Why do you think you became a perfectionist?" he asked.

"Do you really want to know?" I answered. I wanted to be sure he truly wanted to dive into this conversation we'd only tiptoed around for so many years.

When he nodded, I went on, "I think I was protecting myself from my deepest wound, numbing myself from it, hiding it from myself. Whether you and mom meant for it to happen, when you divorced, you left me. Mom left my brother. We were just kids. Our bodies and souls didn't know the difference between intentions and actions. They just felt abandoned."

I didn't go on then, trying to hide the tears that were just under the surface of my now shaky voice. I didn't need to. The look in his eyes told me he understood. My deepest wound was being abandoned so many years ago.

I could have told him about all the lives I'd lived between where we found ourselves on that mountain that day and the day Mom and I drove away in that little, white car—the fear, the lack, the loss, the alcoholics, the repeated abandonment, being alone for so long. I could have. He didn't really know about all of those things either, but he didn't need to. He understood my deepest thorn, I thought, and he could see in the woman I was continuing to become, that I'd dug and dug and dug until I found it. He saw that I'd pulled it out, and hopefully, that I was no longer covering it with a superficial bandage. I wanted him to see and did my best to show him, that I let my deepest cut lay exposed while I learned to care for it and heal from it.

We made it to the top of the pass that day and down the other side of the mountain, our truck tires occasionally struggling to find purchase on the steep, gravel, mountain road. Miraculously, we pulled into a gas station in Prescott, AZ late that afternoon without ever running out of gas. Dad treated me to dinner and a drink that night, a huge prime rib with lots of horseradish and a buttery potato, at a historic, old-timey, western restaurant in town. We sat across from each other, laughing and talking about work, and for maybe the first time, really *seeing* one another.

I've worked at having the same, real moments with my mom too. She meets me at the hospital where my health continues to be monitored by specialists. Most often, we "catch-up"—talk about how everyone is doing and what we're all up to. She's been single for too many years to count now. Occasionally, she makes a joke or a reference to the time in our life that everything got turned upside down. The time before my two younger sisters were born; before her third divorce; before my marriage; before I had two daughters of my own; before she stayed weeks at our house after c-sections and an appendix ruptured to clean and cook and care for us. Mostly, we never even whisper about what happened before all of that, but sometimes it accidentally slips out. When it does, I do my best to be open and honest, to be real. I try to let her know that many of the things she laughs off are not funny to me at all. That's when I see that time, space, the mysteries of the memory, and individual coping mechanisms have left us each with a different interpretation of those moments.

I've never actually had the courage to utter the word abandoned to my mom. I still fear the damage to her and to the relationship we do have left, were I to say those things, a familiar feeling from my teen years. Recently, I did lightly question her about the year my brother and I visited her and Dan in Alamosa over Christmas. I wanted to know if my memory was accurate. This is how I came to understand that she had been forced to go to a therapist by her boss when she was a new dispatcher for the Colorado State Patrol. She explained the ultimatum she was given, after Dan fired the gun in the street on New Year's Eve decades before, while we sat in her driveway for her summer garage sale.

She laughed and used phrases like, "…it was crazy!" and "He (Dan) was so stupid." I did not feel like laughing. The words crazy and stupid didn't feel like the correct adjectives.

During another recent conversation my mom laughed about something I got in trouble for in junior high. She thought it was funny how out of character it was for me to do such a thing, *one of the only times I ever got in trouble in school*, she explained to my aunt through her laughs and her smile. I felt immediately covered in a past sense of shame I thought I had shed. Instead of laughing with her—brushing it off, moving on—I took a deep breath. I remembered who I am, my most real, most wild self. I waited for her to finish, then I said, "You know Mom, that time wasn't funny to me at all. I was crying out for help during one of the worst times in my life."

She stopped laughing then, only briefly looked me in the eyes, before she looked up and said, "It wasn't *that* bad, Debbie." And that was it. That was enough for me. I was reminded of my commitment to myself, to be real, anytime, with anyone, under any circumstance. I would not, will not, go back to where I once was—afraid, alone, hiding, denying, pleasing, perfecting. But I was also reminded of another commitment. If I wanted to have a relationship with my mom—and I do want to have a relationship with my mom (I want a mom)—I've learned that I cannot expect more than she can give. In fact, I've learned to release *all* expectations of my mother. That's part of forgiveness, too.

Forgiveness meant seeing the whole person, Mom and Dad and myself, for all our best and worst, good and bad, love and abandonment, selflessness and selfishness. Seeing *all* of it, rather than focusing only on the ugly. Or, like I'd done for so many years, pretending the ugly never happened at all. It was the pretending that, at least in part, led to my body breaking down and crying for help; the pretending that led to no longer finding purpose or meaning, to giving up, to wanting to die. Forgiveness meant not only seeing all the extremes and in-betweens, but finding the beauty in all the contradictions themselves. It meant learning that it's those contradictions that actually make life so much more *life*. The contradictions are the very, "life of life," as the Sanskrit says. Forgiveness means doing it over and over again, when I forget, when I don't hold a firm boundary, or when I once again feel the pain as though for the first time, which sometimes happens. In those times I remember to see it and release, see it and release, over and over again.

The contradictions of life also help me find the beauty in the whole story, not just parts of it. The moments that wedged that thorn into the deepest part of my soul—the ones so ugly I hid them away from myself and the world for so long out of fear of what might happen if they were exposed—are the same moments that have brought me to the exact place I am now. The thorn hurt. Hiding it away hurt, caused a bigger wound. Only through exposing that wound—the one gaping after digging down so deep, pulling out the thorn, and naming it for what it was—was I able to see just how beautiful and significant the wound could be. It was where the light entered. My deepest empathy, greatest love, truest healing (physical and emotional), most beautiful gifts, those all came from the wound I was no longer afraid to expose, to myself or anyone else. It is all me, the joy and the pain, all made better, so much more real, by the dramatic contradiction.

I have more pain-free days than painful ones now. I still see my specialists in Denver on a regular basis, often enough to get refills on my immunosuppressants and check-in on the status of my heart and lungs. I'm grateful for the information and stability these doctors have afforded me. My cardiologist never lets up about *getting under that rug and sweeping out anything that's been hiding under it*, though he has absolutely no idea just how much I had been keeping under mine. In one of our most recent conversations, while looking over some test results showing abnormalities with my heart, he said, "You know, I think your heart is still a little angry about something, but I don't doubt that you have the power to help it heal itself if you don't give up." I hope my gratitude shown through the tears his words brought to my eyes.

At least two years have passed since I visited the chiropractor. I haven't needed to. I haven't forgotten the first lessons I had in her yellow room, the ones that cracked me open and allowed me to begin letting go. It was in that room that my deepest held pain, physical and emotional, would find the light and the space to leave my body. It's because of those visits that I've let go of control.

I no longer try to control my body by denying it or overworking it. Instead, I do my best to nourish it lovingly by providing conditions that allow it to heal. I no longer try to control the perceptions of others through perfecting my body, my actions, or attempting to perfect the people I love. Instead, I work each day to expose the truest parts of myself willingly in trust, knowing that it will lead me to what is meant for my soul. I no longer try to control the actions of others (happiness, attachment to me, treatment of me) by pleasing them. Instead, I create and maintain boundaries that allow me to find peace regardless of the choices of those I'm surrounded by.

I'm not perfect. I'm not pretending to be. I've walked through that fruitless, soul-sucking search. I'm on the other side now, the other side of perfect, and headed right back to the wild that's been waiting for me all along.

Epilogue

"It's all purification from here on out. A conscious being recognizing that he or she has taken birth and the purpose of their incarnation is to relieve suffering." - Ram Dass

On that day, during my morning meditation—sun streaming through the breaks in the blinds—I saw her. I saw my young self, a little girl with wild, dark hair, still in her nightgown that left her bare legs exposed. She was crying. She was mad. I could feel it. Her fists were balled forcefully at her sides.

In that moment—that dream of a memory, neither past nor present—I felt nothing but warmth and love for that child I once was. I couldn't name or describe all that had happened to her, everything that caused the sad and angry tears. I didn't need to, not anymore. Instead, I spoke softly to her.

You can trust me now, was my answer to her pain. *Come back to me. Let's play together. I'll take care of you this time. I know better.*

She took my hand, and we walked through the door together, right back to the wild.

Stay in touch with Debbie and get your accompanying journal at www.gobucketyourself.com/books, today!

The journal includes all of the prompts found in this book with space to write, as well as extras. You'll find additional journal prompts, other daily journaling suggestions, a reading list, and a musical play-list to guide you through the book and your own, personal healing journey.

Acknowledgments

I am deeply grateful to my husband and partner of nearly two decades, Chris Emick. It is no small feat to support and hold space for someone as they not only embark on self-discovery and healing, but also choose to write a book about it. As months turned into years of the culmination of this project, your enthusiasm, encouragement, and faith in the process and my abilities never waned. Even as I tired of my own words, you never did. Thank you! This would not have been possible without you.

Thank you to my daughters, Claire and Delilah. You are the inspiration and the driving force behind this entire creation. I'm eternally grateful that the two of you gave me a reason to get up off the couch and get serious about becoming whole and breaking cycles. Thank you also for many mornings of making your own breakfast, riding your bike to swimming practice, and several day stretches at home with your father so that I might have the space and time to write. My love for you is deeper and wider than words could ever express. I hope it shows.

To my grandmother and the memory of my grandfather, gratitude doesn't seem enough. You showed me home. You taught me what really mattered. You inspired me to make something of this one, precious life, and you were an example of how I could always find a bit of peace within myself (or at the lake). Thank you.

To Mom, Dad, T.D.R, and the J.L.Bs, I love you all. I'm grateful for you all, now and always.

I thank the women who muddled through the roughest and earliest drafts and helped me craft something better. Lisa Faus, Carrie Doan, Amy Hines, Anna Rider, and Anne Katherine Baptiste; your hours spent reading and responding are not taken lightly. You've all helped in your own way to make the book what it is now. To Diania Merriam, Patricia Mercer, Erin Osterfeld, and Jalea Baker, and again, Carrie Doan, and Lisa Faus. I'm ever so grateful for this circle of women, for your guidance, support, encouragement, and all the time you spent listening to me cry. Thank you for helping me feel like I could do it and telling me it would be okay.

Much thanks to MK Williams, my guide. You know exactly where I'd be without you, because you took this from words on a page to an actual product. Forever and ever, thank you!

Thank you to my editor, Sarah Bruya, for going above and beyond what was asked or required. Thank you to Matt Stone and his team at 100 Covers for a cover that's beyond anything I could have dreamed of myself. And to Giada, I'm so grateful to have a beautiful journal to accompany this book because of you.

My gratitude to you all is beyond measure.

About The Author

Debbie Emick is co-creator and blogger at gobucketyourself.com. She is co-host of the One Life. Live It! podcast. She lives on the planes of southeastern Colorado with her husband, two daughters, Denali the dog, and her six chickens. When she's not traveling to the mountains, the beach, or Spanish-speaking countries, you'll find her there, in her sun room or on her back porch sipping hot tea.

CPSIA information can be obtained
at www.ICGtesting.com
Printed in the USA
LVHW031613290121
677805LV00004B/160